From Colina for my
Birthday July 1946

THEY COME BY APPOINTMENT

by the same author

THE HEALING KNIFE
A SURGEON'S DESTINY
SURGEON'S SYMPHONY
A RING AT THE DOOR
RUSSIA TRIUMPHANT
A TALE OF TEN CITIES
THEY STAYED IN LONDON
SCHOOL FOR WAR
BEAUTY FROM THE SURGEON'S KNIFE
THE CHETNIKS
RASPUTIN SPEAKS
DONKEY SERENADE
WAR WITHOUT GUNS
VALLEY OF FORGOTTEN PEOPLE
TWICE THE CLOCK ROUND
LAND FIT FOR HEROES
LINK OF TWO HEARTS

THEY COME BY APPOINTMENT

by

GEORGE SAVA

FABER AND FABER LTD
24 Russell Square
London

First published in Mcmxlvi
by Faber and Faber Limited
24 Russell Square London W.C.1
Printed in Great Britain by
Purnell and Sons Limited
Paulton (Somerset) and London

This book is produced in complete conformity
with the authorized economy standards

CONTENTS

PROLOGUE

They come by appointment.

You know little or nothing about them. They are just names in the appointments book. Someone speaks to you on the telephone: another consultation. You return from lunch, and your secretary tells you that Mr. Smith or Miss Brown is coming to see you at three-thirty the next day. It was the first free half-hour you had left on that day, and you had hoped to do something about that growing pile of correspondence in arrears . . . But no matter—it is another consultation. For all the personal interest attaching to the case, the name you have just jotted down in your diary might as well be that of the Paramount Chief of some Melanesian island as that of the staid-looking Mrs. White-Jones it is. A name, an entry, a time, a date . . .

Miss Brown may be a devastating beauty or the primmest of middle-aged spinsters. She may be suffering from some rare and dangerous condition, which makes her dear to the eye of the surgeon and raw material for a possible paper in the journals, or she may be a rich hypochondriac. She may even be one of those queer people who think they ought to have an operation so as to have something to talk about at parties, so low has the art of conversation fallen. And Colonel Green may be the very spit of Colonel Blimp, or he may be one of those astonishingly young gentlemen in the twenties who wear the insignia of that rank in combination with the Pegasus of the Airborne forces.

They come by appointment. There is a ring at the bell, and a name is brought into you. A little later, the patient arrives. The name has become a person—very often a frightened person or one ill at ease. It may be a self-confident man with a grand contempt for doctors or a shrinking young lady who seems to think they are a race of gods set apart above men.

Little by little, you hear their stories. You may be their last hope after they have had refusal after refusal from other surgeons. You may be the selected victim of the young lady who knows very well what she wants but is trying hard to simulate appendicitis. Your name may be breathed with ecstasy or barked at you. You may not even be given a name at all, but hidden under the respectable and respectful cloak of "doctor".

Even then they are little more than walking names, fresh cases to whom the same routine of questions has to be put, for whom a new card has to be filled in for the index. They have signs and symptoms—some of them. They may be in search of lost looks or fighting hard and resolutely for a life that is slipping from them. But they are still cases and still types. You have met this person who argues your diagnosis as equal to equal on a good many occasions; you know equally well the one who would accept meekly a verdict of total blindness while he is reading aloud a card of test types.

But little by little something of their personality emerges. They cease to be names and gradually assume the three dimensions of personalities, with their secret fears and hopes, their hidden joys and sorrows. They are people, after all—people of flesh and blood; very often suffering flesh and blood which it is your duty to heal. And step by step you win their confidence, and for the time being you and the patient become parts of a two-person team working for one end—the patient's health and happiness.

They lose their reserve and tell you more about themselves, something more than medical histories, and you look deep into the infinite variety of the human soul. It is then that the final metamorphosis has been made. They are no longer names and cases. They are real individuals who can live in the memory. They tell stories of tragedy and stories of fulfilment, and each is different from the other . . .

PROLOGUE

It is some of those stories I have set down in the following pages. They are medical stories—yes; but they are not mere case histories. They are stories of men and women and children who have come to the surgeon's consulting room as the gateway to release from this or that ill. And all of them brought something more than that ill; for each gave a new glimpse of the thing we call Life, each was a living proof that there are no two people exactly the same in the whole of the millions who walk the earth.

I

"TO BE OR NOT TO BE . . ."

There can be no mistake about it. It was undoubtedly one of my more successful cases. I accepted long odds against pulling it off, and my faith was justified. Such a case always bring a glow of satisfaction to a doctor; it means another life saved, another human being rescued from suffering, another family and circle of friends from which the grim shadow of impending tragedy has been lifted.

Yet it is for none of those reasons that the case remains so deeply inscribed on my memory. Of course, I like to remember the technical aspect of it. Who does not enjoy reflecting upon a piece of work well done? But it is for the fascinating personality, the almost fantastic atmosphere, that I regard this case as noteworthy and worthy of something more than my own private thoughts and a cold entry in my casebook. So it is—or should be—with all one's cases. Memories of the people should remain long after the technical details have become dim. The doctor, no matter whether his practice lies in Harley Street or Hoxton, whether he be general practitioner or specialist, who allows every newcomer to his consulting room to be no more than "another case" ends up by being a bad doctor—if he is not already one to start with.

My first introduction to Mr. William Latty was through his daughter, whom I had met informally somewhere or another. She was looking, I remember, worried and depressed. There was something, I could see, weighing heavily on her mind. There was no topic of conversation that could hold her attention for long. After a little while the shadow came over her face again and her dark thoughts, whatever they might be, oppressed her, occupying her whole attention.

I felt sorry for her but there was nothing I could do about it. After all, what greater impertinence is there than to pry into another's private worries, unasked? Besides, one of the earliest lessons I learnt on coming to this country was that the English like to keep their sorrows to themselves and that indiscreet inquiries, however well intentioned, are usually met with that "Oh, nothing's the matter, really. A bit under the weather, I suppose"—which is the most crushing recommendation to mind one's own business that I know.

I talked to her as best I could, thinking that I might distract her a little and turn those brooding thoughts away from their focus, if only for a moment or two. And as so often happens, she felt my unspoken sympathy and quite suddenly, without warning, began to tell me all about it. She did so diffidently, and I think a natural reluctance to be suspected of cadging for professional advice held her back a little.

"It's a horrible thing," she said, commenting on her own thoughts, which had no kind of connection with what we had been discussing, "when you've got to sit back and watch someone you're very fond of die before your eyes."

I looked at her in some surprise. This glimpse of what was distressing her took me off my guard.

"It is," I replied, rather unhelpfully. I waited and did not press. If she wished to tell me, it would come of its own accord.

"It's my father," she said slowly, after a thoughtful pause.

"He is seriously ill?" I asked.

She nodded. "Hopelessly. I have done everything. He has been X-rayed and I suppose there's no escape from it. Cancer, doctor." She shuddered. It is the disease people fear most. The very word makes the bravest shiver: cancer—the crab whose pitiless claws can so rarely be loosened once they have taken a firm hold. The one thing is to kill the creature as soon as its nippers give the first pinch. "They say it is inoperable."

I expressed my sympathy. I wanted to help her. What doctor does not wish he had a magician's wand when he hears those words "inoperable—incurable" uttered in his presence? One feels as though one has been personally indicted in the name of the whole profession, the whole science and art of medicine.

She told me more about her father.

"He is so resigned," she said. "He takes it all so philosophically. But then he has good friends." She smiled rather sadly.

"Friends are a great blessing," I returned.

"They are not ordinary human friends," she explained. "They were born three hundred years ago, and they live today—particularly for him. You know, doctor, he is a great Shakespearian. He knows the plays by heart, and I think the characters, great and small, are the only real things in the world for him."

I opened my eyes a little. I have met all sorts and conditions of men but I have not mixed much with great scholars.

"He is a professor—a lecturer?" I inquired.

She laughed. It was the first time I had seen her amused that day. The dark expression lifted momentarily from her face.

"No," she said, shaking her head. "He has no use for these people who tear Shakespeare to pieces, as he puts it. The plays are living things to him. No, daddy's no professor," she went on. "He's nothing at all wonderful. He just keeps a shop—and by the way it's not so far from your hospital."

I was interested. A shopkeeper who knew the plays of Shakespeare by heart, who lived in a world peopled by the greatest characters in drama, was certainly a novelty to me. But I could not seek to gratify my curiosity then. It was time for me to go. I said good-bye to her, murmuring some commonplace hopes that even the best of doctors has been sometimes proven wrong. And in the next few days, in the press of work, I admit I practically forgot the shopkeeping Shakespearian. After all, daughters, especially those as fond of their fathers as this one was, often magnified their father's abilities; the trick of being able to quote a few lines might well be the factual basis for this legend I had heard . . . An ungenerous thought, one of which I am now ashamed, but perhaps not unnatural.

Destiny ordained that I was to meet this scholar of the stores. And the appointed time came soon. I was summoned to see an urgent case, not at the hospital but at his home . . A Mr. William Latty . . . I groped in my memory to explain the familiarity this name had for me. Latty? Oh, yes, of course: the Shakespearian . . .

His daughter admitted me to the small, attractive house. She spoke to me quickly, quietly, and seriously. Her father was very, very ill. I had been called in as a last desperate resort. She trusted me. If I said that nothing could be done, then she would accept it as final. And while she talked I let myself unobtrusively take in the atmosphere of the room. Yes, it was a scholar's room, with shelves filled with Shakespeariana. The plays in many editions, old and new; commentaries; the monographs of theorists and speculators: there were books everywhere, but only on one subject, that which for two centuries and more has provided scholars and pedants, essayists and doctrinaires, with an inexhaustible mine: William Shakespeare, the poet and dramatist whose works are familiar to many peoples and many lands, but whose life and the manner of it remain as obscure as the very cause of genius itself.

But my presence there was not due to an interest in Shakespeare; I was there as a surgeon urgently summoned to a serious case; and I asked to be taken at once to the patient. He was in bed, and my heart sank as I glanced at his face. It was quiet, almost serene in expression, though perhaps not at all remarkable in its features. On it were the marks that I had come to know only too well, the scorings that are carved by the first tentative graspings of the hand of death.

He smiled at me, and I began my examination. Once more my heart sank. I knew what the X-ray photographs had shown, but this was a case in which X-rays were but a confirmation. Those diagnosticians of a past generation, who, with their sensitive fingers, their appraising eyes, and clear logical minds, knew nothing of the aids we modern doctors regard as essential, would have had no doubt about this case. It presented no difficulty at all. Below the costal margin was a lump that even the least experienced fingers could detect. It was one of the largest I had ever felt. Yes, it was a desperate case. Inoperable? Yes, of course.

All the time he had lain back in perfect relaxation, offering no comments, concerned, so it seemed, just with the act of breathing. And then his voice came to me, clearly, distinctly, and cut through the dark cloud of thought that wrapped me. It was his voice; but the words were the words of Shakespeare, famous above even the many famous lines of that superb poet with whom England enriched the world: the words of Hamlet:

"*To be or not to be . . .*"

He went on, savouring the words on his palate, like a connoisseur with his Château-Yquem. How many times had he read and quoted those words, I wondered. Yet one could hear that they were ever fresh to him, that every time he recalled them he saw some new beauty in their form, some new profundity in their thought, as a lover sees ever some new enchantment in his mistress.

"*To be or not to be—that is the question—*
Whether 'tis nobler in the mind to suffer
The slings and arrows of outrageous fortune . . ."

Here, in truth, were the slings and arrows of outrageous fortune! But they were only indirectly of the mind; perhaps not there. For this man had the philosophy of the master in whose steps he followed. One believed he would face death without a qualm, like Hamlet himself.

"*Or to take arms against a sea of troubles,*" he continued—
And by opposing end them . . .?"

That was my question, not his. Here indeed was a sea of troubles. Had I the arms to oppose them?

". . . To die—to sleep—
No more; and by a sleep to say we end
The heartache and the thousand natural shocks
That flesh is heir to . . ."

Was he consciously putting his case to me through these immortal words? The alternatives were put plainly before me, with a vividness nothing could have brightened. On the one side, death; on the other vigorous action. And the weariness, the yearning to die—to sleep—was that, too, an expression of his own deep longing? Did he feel that it was time to cry "Enough!"—and with it perhaps the doubt whether he had the courage for death?

A doctor must order his conduct by the rules of science. But he is also a human being, in whom are the same dark wellsprings of thought and action as other men know. Perhaps because his experience of humanity—and particularly suffering humanity—is wider than most men's, he becomes hypersensitive. He has to make bold and big decisions that may mean the saving of a life—or its cessation. Science, the cold logic of the laboratory, has not the answer to all his problems, particularly if he is a surgeon. For to a surgeon the last question is always: Can I do it? His knowledge and experience may tell him that such and such a thing is possible. But beyond that is his own skill and whether it can turn possibility into actuality.

I do not say that it was the magic of Hamlet's words that led me to my decision, but I do say that their coming at that time focused my mind precisely on the questions at issue. Surely this was a case of to be or not to be—and that question could not be left to resolve itself but had to be tackled at once.

So it was that, in that minute, I determined upon a bold course. Some perhaps may call it foolhardy, but I do not think so. As I saw it there was a ray of hope; and if there is such a ray it is not for the doctor to pull down the blinds; rather he should seek to turn it into a bright gleam that grows. "Inoperable" is a big word I do not like. It does not mean quite what it says, for it suggests a knowledge—an omnipotence—among the medical profession that those with the widest experience would be the last to claim. What it means in the vast majority of cases is that those who pronounce it do not think they have the skill necessary to do the work in hand—or that our knowledge is so limited that none of us knows the way. And it is that which makes so many dubious about the rightness of euthanasia—but this is digressing from my theme.

There was that chance and I resolved to take it. I would, if the patient and his family consented, open the abdomen and then with the full facts before me decide what could be done. Had he the courage? I thought so. And I believed, too, that it was my duty to explain to him personally what I proposed to do, exaggerating rather than minimizing the risks, leaving no possible doubt in his mind that the possible —nay the probable—result was death.

For the first time he spoke to me. It was almost as though he had divined my thoughts.

"It's hopeless, doctor?" he asked.

"Not quite as bad as that," I replied, though in a serious voice. "I think there is a faint ray of hope, but the risk is enormous and the odds against success are very long. The question is whether you're prepared to take the risk."

"What does it matter, doctor?" he returned with a resigned air. "If I am to die, I must die. It makes no difference whether I go now, with you making a fight for me, or if I wait till that thing kills me."

"It is a very serious operation," I insisted, "that I propose to make. Almost, but not quite, a counsel of despair."

He smiled faintly and replied in the words of Shakespeare; it was as though quotation was more habitual to him than ordinary speech.

"*Diseases desperate grown,*
By desperate appliances are relieved," he said. *Hamlet* again.

"True. Would you like to talk it over with your daughter? There is no need to make an emergency operation of it, you know."

"No thanks, doctor. I know she would like me to take the risk, as you put it, though to me all thought of risk has gone. When there's a certainty before you, the only thing is choice of means. But I have one request to make."

"Yes?" I did not quite know what to expect. Patients sometimes make the most curious requests on these occasions, and I am never surprised at what they ask.

"Can it be next week?"

I thought quickly and nodded. "Yes. I think it can be arranged at the hospital."

"Thank you. I have a special reason for that," he explained. "You see, next week I shall be seventy-two, and if I must die I'd rather die on my birthday. Shakespeare did, so they say, but that's absurd, because he can never die. No, my reason is more practical. I don't want people arguing about my age. So if it's next Wednesday, they can say I died on my seventy-second birthday, without any months or days. Besides, it would finish off the whole business very tidily, and I've always been a tidy man."

"Very well." It was a request I had never had before, but it was typical of the man, concerned not with what he evidently considered the almost certain fact of death but with its seemly occurrence. He had nurtured his mind and soul on the perfection of a poet's creation and he wished his own humble life to be some faint echo of it.

"I shall give you a local anæsthetic," I said, discussing the necessary details with him. "It is the better way at your age. It may take a long time."

"Yes, I am glad of that. I think I should prefer it like that."

And so after a little more talk I left him. The words of the Soliloquy were still ringing in my ears. I was embarking on an "enterprise of great pith and moment" in earnest. Yet I had no doubts. I did not disguise to myself that the chances of success were extremely small; that would have been the height of foolishness. But I was glad that I had made up my mind to seize that small chance to do with it what I might. His quiet courage in the face of what was almost certain death, his sure mastery of himself, his natural faith: these were things worth making a fight for, worth trying to preserve in a world in which hate and destruction and death were rampant.

He already interested me deeply as a person and not simply as a case presenting very special anxieties and problems, and in the few days before he came into hospital I learnt a little more of him. It was chiefly of his immense Shakespearian knowledge. I had heard him quote one of the most famous of all the familiar passages of Shakespeare. I had heard him make use of two lines from the same play—which, incidentally, expressed more picturesquely an aphorism of one of the earliest medical authorities in the world, Hippocrates. By itself that was no test of wide Shakespearian learning. But now I gathered that all the plays were his province, that he was as familiar with the lines and characters of such minor people as Audrey in *As you Like It* as with the cosmic reflections of Hamlet or the symbolical imagery of Prospero. The plays were his life; and I began to feel, in an odd sort of way, that to save his life was to save, too, something of the eternal Shakespearian tradition—a tradition whose force I had first felt personally even through the barriers that translation into Russian and other Slav tongues set up. For that is the supreme wizardry of Shakespeare's creations. A master of words, almost the maker of a new language, so did he vitalize English, his characters and thoughts and philosophy shine through even an alien idiom of speech and thought.

There was little opportunity of thinking of Shakespeare, however, when he was brought into the theatre. I made the incision, and desperate though I knew the case to be I was perhaps not quite prepared for what was now revealed. The growth was larger than I had any reason to expect, and the whole of the pylorus—the connexion between the stomach and the intestine—was involved. The obstruction was complete, and if it had been left, death would not have been long delayed.

For two hours we worked on that operation. The patient was, of course, conscious all the time, though he felt nothing, and I was never more grateful for the gift of local anæsthetics. I doubt if a man of his age and low condition could have withstood a long period of total anæsthesia, and I should have had to work against the clock, which would in all probability have destroyed that one faint chance of success—a chance that looked, now I knew all, even ridiculously smaller than ever.

For some time, William Latty, the quiet Shakespearian with the soul of a hero, lay quiet behind the drapes that shield the field of the operation from the sight of the patient when a local anæsthetic is employed. Then, when the very climax of the work had been reached, I heard his voice. It was the same voice I had heard when I had been called to his house—a voice that was his, yet which also suggested that it came from something deep within his soul, bigger than himself. But this time it was not the tortured perplexities of a Hamlet; it was the bold challenging apostrophe of John of Gaunt—lines that have during the past few years been more often quoted than ever before, and yet, despite that fact, retain all their marvellous lustre, like a gold coin in constant circulation.

This royal throne of kings, this sceptred isle,
This earth of majesty, this seat of Mars,
This other Eden, demi-paradise . . .

In that setting, the famous words acquired a new and strange significance. It was John of Gaunt speaking, the outburst of a courageous spirit making an exultant appeal against the degradation that he sees before him.

I have begun the quotation at its most familiar place, but Latty started it from the beginning; and at the very first line it started in my head, though never to the point of distracting attention from what I was doing, vivid thoughts.

. . . insatiate cormorant
Consuming means, soon preys upon itself

—how better to describe this cancer, devouring the very vitals of this man? The words, so far from disturbing me, seemed to heighten my sensibility, so that I saw with a more penetrating eye, thought with a more perceptive mind. Above all I saw again how important it was to save this life . . .

They have always been for me the most glorious lines in all Shakespeare. The little highbrows may decry them, spurning their glowing patriotism, shrugging their shoulders because they are hackneyed. But are they not rather the evocation of a spirit than the "propagandist blather of imperialism", as I have heard them described? Does a pearl, a diamond, a ruby, become hackneyed, merely because it it is often worn and delighted in? And now they have forever for me a deeper significance. They call to mind that strange scene, where among all the sterile scientific trappings of the operating theatre the magic of great art suddenly blossomed forth and gave everything a new purpose.

Was he, I wondered, convinced now that all was vain, that the faint spark of hope had glowed less redly and gone out? I almost thought so, for there was a curious quality of intenseness as he came to the two final lines:

Ah! would the scandal vanish with my life
How happy then would be my ensuing death.

It might have been so. But on me the words had the effect of increasing my resolve that there must be no ensuing death, that I must give more than I had ever given before to make certain that this man who could beckon to death with the gigantic phrase of blank verse should have the right again to welcome life . . .

At last it was over. The final suture was closed. I had done all I could do, used every bit of skill and knowledge I possessed. And what now? It had been a major operation

—a very major operation. It had necessarily been a heavy shock to a system that was inevitably weak with age, and that had been still further weakened by this malignant growth. The testing time had yet to come. And perhaps the final outcome lay in his hands, for if his courage failed, if his belief in life vanished, then, do what we might with all the resources of a great hospital, death would probably claim what I had fought so hard to save.

Those post-operative hours and days are always the most anxious time. It is then that the idiosyncrasy of the patient shows itself. Failure sometimes comes during that trying time when success seems assured; and sometimes, more happily, the apparently hopeless stages an almost startling recovery. It is these things which preserve one's proper sense of humility in the presence of that complex thing we call a human being, a thing we analyse and dissect but never quite succeed in understanding.

With William Latty it was, of necessity, a stern fight, a grim and bitter struggle. He had a blood transfusion, but even then the issue hung in doubt. And then the miracle happened. It was as though he had been a beleaguered city valiantly holding out against the forces of destruction and the siege had been suddenly lifted. From then on, it was a long struggle, but never again was the outcome in doubt.

Yes, it was one of the cases where the long odds had not proved too heavy, a case which anyone might have been excused for refusing. But I do not claim that it was a masterpiece of skill on my part. The final victory, the recovery, was due to his indomitable spirit, his belief in life; and perhaps the boldness which had inspired me, the determination I had shown to bring him through, had been due to those lines of Shakespeare. For, as I said before, the surgeon is a human being and the limits and possibilities of his powers cannot be marked out with the precision of the properties of a chemical, and his resources are not entirely those with which the textbook and the lecture theatre and his own practice provide him.

It was some time after I had ceased attending him and had written him off in my casebook—though not in my memory—that his daughter came to see me. She was still full of gratitude as she had been at the time when we felt sure of his recovery; and she would not listen to my contentions that the triumph had been in her father's own serene and fearless soul. She persisted in regarding me as a miracle-worker—a role which, with vivid memories of the Russia of my childhood's days, I have no ambition to fulfil. But she had not come to give thanks to me again. This time it was business.

"We can never repay you, doctor," she said earnestly. "There is no price for life. But there is something we can do—and you have never sent in your bill. Let me know what your fee is—and excuse me for being so blunt."

I refused her offer point-blank.

"No," she insisted. "That isn't right. You have given us one priceless thing. Don't give us any more."

It was not a case for a fee, and I told her so.

"Listen," I said. "This wasn't an ordinary case. It was a very great experience for me. Try and look at it in this way. Your father, through his courage, gave me an opportunity of carrying out an operation such as would very rarely come my way. My debt is to him, and you have none to me. He is a textbook case."

She smiled. "That's very tactfully put, doctor, and I appreciate it. But I still think it isn't fair. Let me at least pay some of the expenses. I know I can't hope to pay them all—but something."

I shook my head. "No, though I do understand and appreciate your attitude, Miss Latty. You said just now you were under a debt you could never repay. I don't agree. But even if it were so, I, too, owe a debt to you which cannot be repaid. So the obligation is mutual and cancels out."

"So you won't be shifted," she returned. "You are still harping on the textbook case, I suppose?"

"No," I said seriously. "It is something much greater than that, though that is important. It is that through you I have got to know a very remarkable personality—a man of courage and unconquerable spirit."

She looked at me and rose to go; and I believe there were tears in her eyes.

Nor was that the end.

One night I arrived home to find a mysterious package awaiting me. I was expecting nothing, and I could not guess what it might be. Luckily I am not eminent enough to fear the bomb by post which, writers of spy stories tell us, is a commonplace of the mailbags of the great. But when I had undone the string and slipped the wrappings away, my eyes almost started from my head.

There was no need to consult the slip to see where this had come from. No other man than William Latty would have given such a gift, or made so stupendous a gesture of appreciation and thanks. For the first time I held an early Folio of the Works of William Shakespeare in my hand.

I know that if I sent it to the saleroom, it would bring me an enormous price. I know that many a library would bless me unceasingly if I sent it to them on loan. I know that merely to turn its pages would be paradise for a thousand poor scholars.

But it is for none of those things that this Folio ranks among my most treasured possessions. It is the thought behind it, the gesture of a man who could give—and gladly—that which in itself was most precious to him, and which held for him the wisdom of the world. And I treasure it, too, because of the man himself, the man who could bring from its cold, antique print some of its most wonderful lines and make them live when the very breath of his life was seeping from him.

All that was three years ago. His seventy-fifth birthday was celebrated just when I was starting out to write of this. For me the occasion was marked by an unsigned card with two lines upon it. They needed no signature:

For, from this instant
There's nothing serious in mortality.

II

A LATE DECISION

The plastic surgeon is as much a mender of minds as a mender of bodies. He is concerned, as often as not, with the creation of a comeliness that either Nature has denied or accident has destroyed, and by so doing he often takes away more than the disfiguring scar and the twisted feature. For with these blemishes go a haunting sense of inferiority, an unwillingness for their possessors to mix with their fellow beings. It is, perhaps, this which brings patients to the plastic surgeon more compellingly than the mere desire for beauty. The actress or model who breaks her nose stands in danger of losing her livelihood—and with it her self-respect; the plastic surgeon can save both. And in this last terrible war, his skill has been the means whereby hundreds of young men, scarred, burnt, and battered, have been restored to a state in which they can again take part in everyday life—instead of being condemned, as many were after the 1914 war, to homes where the only hope of release was death and the present was a nightmare of mental agony.

Yes, it is psychological reasons that bring men and women to the plastic surgeon. Just because of that it is precisely plastic cases that provide so much interesting material for the student of humanity—which every doctor must be. Frequently he has the joy of knowing that he has been the means of bringing back some blemished man or woman to his full rights as a human being; and that is the doctor's greatest reward, whether he be physician or surgeon. But there are times, too, when—human affairs being the wayward things they are—that which was designed to afford happiness seems to carry in it the seeds of tragedy. I wish I knew which way the signpost of Fate was finally going to point for Mary Baxter.

I can see her now as she was ushered into my consulting-room by the receptionist, for she made a great impression on me. Usually it is the first meeting with people of forceful personality that remains graven on the memory, but it was otherwise with Mary Baxter. She had no personality at all —no, that is an exaggeration: she suggested that her personality had been so long held in check and thrust into the background that it had lost all power to express itself.

She came into the room shyly and quietly, as though she had no right at all to be there. It was not that my presence or the trappings of my room—which is not designed to impress anyway—overwhelmed her; one felt simply that she was the sort of person who really believed she had no right to go where other people went as a matter of course, or to leave her own well-beaten and sheltered paths.

I remembered, as I tried to put her at her ease, the words of the friend who had recommended her to come and see me. "She's a very retiring girl", that friend had said. "You may find it difficult to make her talk. She'll probably agree with everything you say, not because she hasn't got a will of her own, but because she hates to think she's making herself conspicuous. I hope you can do something for her—she's a sweet child, really." My friend is a person of some discernment, and whose judgment of people is usually fairly penetrating and always sound; and I felt that once again she had summed someone up perfectly. Mary Baxter was precisely the girl I should have expected from that description.

In the course of his practice, a doctor grows used to handling people of all kinds: the bumptious, assertive fellow who, in the American phrase, "knows it all", so that one might be excused for wondering why he deigned to consult a doctor at all; the taciturn patient from whom the most commonplace information has to be dragged almost by main force; the frightened patient who feels that the more he says the more terrible one's diagnosis will be; the sceptical fellow who "doesn't believe in doctors" and is mildly amused in a superior way at everything in the consultation. There are all these and many other varieties, and there are as many ways of dealing with them. Some have to be kept well in hand, others cajoled, still others treated almost brutally—yes, I admit it.

It was easy to place Mary Baxter in her proper category. She was suffering from an acute and almost paralysing feeling of inferiority, which clogged even her physical movements, for she had even a walk that was timid and tentative. She was like a creature of the night brought out suddenly into the broad light of noon, and longing again for the sheltering cloak of darkness beneath which to escape all notice.

And the reason for all these things was plainly written on her face. Nature had never intended her to be a raving beauty or to make of her a model that artists would seek from the four corners of the earth. Equally Nature had never intended her to be like this; Fate had taken a hand in the game. At some time—I guessed a long time ago—she had been badly burnt; and the old scar on her cheek disfigured her face, robbing it of all its potential charm. Nor had the mischief ended there. Her nose, too, had been broken and badly set, so that it was distorted and awry. These blows had robbed her of all her confidence; and without confidence in herself, a woman loses all faith in life.

I put her at her ease gradually and won her confidence. As so often happens when a retiring person is concerned, once that barrier of self-depreciation has been pushed aside, she began to talk quite freely, telling the whole background of her life and why she had come to me. It was an interesting story, not only for its facts but also in its self-revelations.

The Baxters had once been the dominant family in part of one of the southern counties, and to the time of Mary's grandfather had been lords of the manor. But evil times came to them as to all the old landed families, and the estate had had to be broken open. On the lodge gates of the Hall, the Baxter arms, carved in the stone, still looked out on the road, as they had for centuries; but the broad drive, with its avenue of beeches, led now to a country club, where the sons and daughters of the new aristocracy of wealth amused themselves in ways that would have seemed strange to the man who had built the Hall and invited his friend the Duke of York, who became James II, to the house-warming.

But Captain Ronald Baxter, Mary's father, could not break the family association with the place. He retained a relatively small portion of the estate and farmed it. He might not now be lord of the manor, but country traditions die hard, and it needs more than sports cars and squash courts to kill them. He was still the Baxter of the Hall, and the country people still looked on him as their leader, one who in some way was set a little apart from them and above them.

Mary had never known the Hall. She had been born and brought up in the mellow old Georgian farm-house that was now the Baxters' home, and from her earliest days she had lived near the land. The old social barriers had broken down to a large extent, and it was only in some mystical way that the Baxters held their old position.

"I'm so glad I never lived in the Hall," said Mary slowly and with pensive eyes. "I should have hated it. All that sort of thing is so silly, isn't it? I mean, people are people wherever they're born and whatever their parents happen to be, aren't they? And to think that the villagers used to curtsey to grandfather when they met him!"

She was a child of the years between the wars. It is a curious thing that the tabus of caste are most easily shed by those who, in days gone by, used most to benefit by them. To herself, Mary Baxter was just Mary Baxter, a girl who lived in the country, worked about the farm and helped to manage it as the daughter of her father; yet to many of those about her, she was the rightful occupant of the Hall and owner of the lands about it—and therefore entitled to a special distinction.

She had been in her middle teens when the first accident happened. There had been a village celebration and a great bonfire had been built. I do not remember the exact occasion, but I believe it was either the Jubilee of George V or the Coronation of George VI. Things had grown lively, and for some reason she never discovered there was a sudden movement of the whole mass of revellers. She was swept before it, unable to stand aside—and had been pitched into the gigantic fire. The results of that tragic affair still remained upon her cheek.

A couple of years later, Fate had struck again. This time tragedy came in a farm lorry. She was riding on it along a narrow lane, where there was little enough room, and one of the sports cars from the country club had come suddenly round a bend, travelling very fast. The lorry driver had swerved onto the grass verge. His coolness saved what would in all probability have been a fatal crash. But the vehicle rammed a telegraph post, and from the wreckage, Mary was brought out with a broken nose.

Mary had enjoyed those days before the war. The land was in her blood. She liked the people working on the farm, even though some of them paid her a deference she regarded as unnecessary and stupid. And there was one she very specially liked. And it was here again and for the third time that the horn-call of tragedy sounded in her life.

James Hoyle was the son of the foreman of the estate. He was about the same age as Mary, and they had known each other from childhood. Their interest was mutual, but they had been kept apart to a large extent by James's father, Walter.

Walter Hoyle was a countryman of the old school, steeped in all the traditions of his county. His family had served the Baxters for generations. They had been born on the Baxter land, worked on the Baxter land, and eventually buried under the Baxter land, in the knowledge that they had left behind other Hoyles to carry on the work. To Walter Hoyle, a Baxter was a Baxter and a Hoyle a Hoyle, less reconcilable than east and west, each moving in an orbit that was no more likely to intercept the other than the orbits of the planets were. So it had been established by some providence he never sought to define or perhaps even to think about. The mere idea that his own son might marry a

Baxter never so much as entered his head, and the curious thing is that, if his son had, Walter Hoyle would probably have considered his family shamed and degraded, such is the queerness of English caste tradition.

Young James Hoyle had freed himself of much of his father's prejudice. But he still felt that the gulf between his family and Mary's was one that could not be bridged. He was, too, sufficiently old-fashioned, as the result of his upbringing, to hold that his father's word was law—and he knew well enough what Walter Hoyle would say if the idea was even mentioned as a joke. James Hoyle marry a Baxter? It was blasphemy.

In her halting, hesitant way, with many digressions, Mary told me all this, though not in the same words. She suggested quite a lot by her manner. Often an unfinished sentence was more significant than a complete one. She revealed much by what she omitted to put into plain words.

I gathered the very clean impression that there was a vicious circle at work, for the absurd class-consciousness of James Hoyle was not the only irrational factor at work. The boy no doubt played down his feelings, for his own curious reasons. No doubt he was cold when he would have been hot, restrained when a less inhibited man would have slackened the rein. He must have given a picture of a reluctant lover—if indeed one of a lover at all.

Mary was at an age when she was most hypersensitive in her relations to men. She was already scarred and her nose deformed. These were burdens difficult for any girl to bear at a time when she was coming to the splendour of her first blossoming. The effect of James's misguided reticence must have been disastrous. Already rendered shy and retiring by her blemishes, Mary now began to believe that he had held aloof from her as he did because of her ugliness. She believed that he liked her, but also that he could not allow his liking to mature into love because her very features were distasteful to him. What agonies of mind she must have endured at this time, none can know but herself; and she is not likely to repeat them to anyone. But one can guess vaguely at them—yet not so vaguely that one fails to obtain an idea of how real and terrifying they must have been.

"He likes me," she must have thought. "He's nice to me. But he can't bear my face. Oh, God, how cruel it is!"

How all this would have developed, if the war had not intervened, it is impossible to guess. Perhaps James's feelings would one day have got the better of his upbringing, and he would have overborne them. One cannot say. If, even then, he had told her that he loved her and asked her to help him to reason with his father, much good would have been done. Not only would Mary's doubts have been removed, but she would have been given back that priceless possession of self-confidence. *Then* it would have been "He loves me in spite of my scars"—and she would have felt that she could face all the world, unafraid and unashamed. But he did not. The more he withdrew from her, the stronger her convictions grew that she was repugnant to him, and the more retiring she became. No doubt her growing self-consciousness of repulsiveness gave him doubts, and any ideas he might have formed about breaking away from his father must have weakened.

All this is idle speculation, though it always fascinates me to carry a line of psychological reasoning through to the end. The crisis of this relationship never came—in that form. Instead came the war—the war that was to destroy so much, good and bad, and give to many a new and perhaps better set of values, while to others it seemed to sweep away all values whatsoever.

James was among the earliest to be called up, and he was posted to an infantry unit. For years he remained in this country, training and re-training, exercising, manœuvring. He rose to the rank of sergeant. Often during these years of waiting and preparation he came home on leave, but now he seemed quite out of Mary's reach. He was no longer just Walter Hoyle's son. He was one of "our boys", a hero to whom all due homage must be paid. The girls in the village and in the small market town near by made eyes at him, and Mary felt, with a pang in her heart, that her dream was no more than a dream. How could she compete with the prettiest girls around?

Yet he always came to see her as much as he could, and he seemed happy and contented when he was with her. She drew no balm from the fact. Her outlook was now almost as warped as her poor, damaged face. He only did so because he wished to be kind to her—that was how she thought of it. And these meetings became bitter-sweet to her, something to which she looked forward with both joy and dread intermingled.

When he was away she wrote to him, and he always replied, cheerfully and in the most friendly way, though always, she felt, there was something a little distant in his letters. To her the reason was obvious; he did not wish to give her any chance to imagine things; she was repulsive to him.

Other forces were at work. He had got away now from all the influences of the narrow thought of a country village. His outlook broadened. He had authority of his own, and was no longer prepared to believe that his father spoke with the word of inviolable law. His letters grew warmer. At times, it seems, they were tinged with the glow of passion.

As she told me this, she blushed and held her head down. Probably to no-one had she confessed as much before. She was ashamed. Did I think her romantic and silly?

I hastened to reassure her. I was glad at the news.

The years came round to 1944. All the world knew that the Allied Armies were preparing for the Invasion, but none knew when or where it would fall. And James knew that when the time came, his unit, which had waited and trained for so long, would be at the spearhead. He had leave and he believed it was the last before he went. Anyway there would be no more leave till after the Invasion, whenever that might be. And in the quiet of an early spring night he talked to Mary. No, he did not propose to her.

There was still something of the old restraint in his manner. The old inhibitions still clung to him a little perhaps; or it may be that he feared he might not come back from the task that lay ahead. He had said one thing to her which remained like a guiding light in her mind:

"When this lot is over," he had said, "you and I must get things straightened out."

It was as near to a promise as he had ever come.

They spent the greater part of that last leave together, and her heart sang. It was all coming right at last! If only her face was not so ugly . . .

James Hoyle crossed the Channel on D-Day. From time to time letters came from him, more lover-like than any he had ever written before, yet always they seemed to Mary to be evading something, as though there was one subject he did not wish to speak about. And to her, with the acute sensitiveness she had developed, that meant her looks. He had not yet the courage to say that he loved her, but for her features.

It was then she heard about plastic surgery from a friend, who was also a friend of mine—a lady who had been one of my patients for a minor plastic operation. Mary's heart leapt. Here was her chance, she thought.

"And that," she said quietly, "is why I have come to you. I should like to look better for his sake. Not for mine. I don't care much what I look like, but if it would please him . . ." She made an expressive gesture and looked shyly at me. "Do you think anything can be done? Please—*please* don't disappoint me."

"I don't think it will be so very difficult," I replied with a smile.

It was not a specially out-of-the-way case. The scar, for all its age, could be excised and a new skin graft made, though it was in a position where a very slight hairbreadth scar might show. The nose could easily be straightened and built up slightly.

I told her all this. "But don't go away from here with big ideas," I warned her. "I don't even promise that I can make you tolerably beautiful. You mustn't expect to look in your glass and see a film-star reflected in it. But you'll have no scars and your nose will be the right shape and proportions for your face."

"Do you really mean it, doctor?" she asked, her eyes shining. "Oh, that would be wonderful! Don't worry—I don't want to be beautiful. It means far more to me that you can get rid of the scar!"

We made some preliminary arrangements, and she promised to come back a few days later to fix the final details.

When she had gone, I mused on her story. It was a fine example of the curious psychological reactions deformity can bring, for all the time she had shown clearly that she suffered a sense of guilt because of unsightliness that was caused through no fault of hers. Even now, when all seemed promising, doubts kept crossing her mind. Whatever the final outcome of her affair with James Hoyle, I thought, if I can rid her of that ridiculous fantasy I shall do well.

When she came back to see me, she was much more cheerful. I had given her hope—and, too, she had heard again from James, the nicest letter she had ever had, though she did not tell me what was in it. Now, she was more anxious than ever to get the operations over as soon as she could. She had talked to her father, and he had appeared very glad she was going to do something for herself at last. After the long days of cloud, the sun was shining on her and everything was right with the world.

It was a fairly long job to do all I wanted to do. Three operations were needed to remove that hideous scar and graft on skin to replace it. And when that was done, there was the nose to deal with. At first I had thought it could be corrected very simply, but after studying the photographs I had had made of her, I decided it was better to embark upon a complete reconstruction. A small piece of bone was removed from one of her ribs, and this was implanted in the nose, the skin being grafted round and the final scars made practically inconspicuous. Luckily she was a good patient. She showed no tendency to the formation of that hard scar tissue known as keloid, which is the bane of the plastic surgeon in his work; for its appearance can set at naught all the thought and care that have been taken to make as certain as may be that old scars shall not be replaced by new ones. I admit that when at last all was finished, I felt I had done a good job.

It was true I had not converted her into a beauty. No plastic surgeon can work miracles. But now she was not at all unattractive. Not a few women would have envied her.

But the most remarkable change was not in the mere details of her face. I always think that the most wonderful part of a reconstruction of this kind is the alteration it produces in expression and to some extent, too, in behaviour. Mary Baxter was a new woman. She was no longer afraid of herself or ashamed of herself. Her eyes glowed with life and happiness and hope. She no longer came into a room as though she was on sufferance. And I thought again as I watched her that my knife had taken away more than that scar. I had cut out a malignant growth that was none the less deadly because it had neither form nor substance and lay entirely in her mind. Perhaps the psychiatrist and the plastic surgeon, both late-comers to the field of curative medicine and both still somewhat suspect in certain non-progressive circles, have something more in common than most people suppose.

I knew what she was thinking as she left me after my final examination of her to see that all was well. She believed now that the last barrier between her and James had been removed, and that when the war was over, they could pass along the path to happiness together. And I, being Russian and therefore at times sentimental, felt glad that I had been able to assist in moulding a happy ending to another tale.

Fate however does not let her chosen victims escape so easily as that. If lightning never strikes twice in the same place, Destiny's arrows seem attracted again and again to the same target. They had wounded Mary Baxter cruelly in her youth, and it had been my privilege to bring about her rehabilitation. It was not enough. Melodrama itself at its ripest could hardly have provided a more dramatic denouement to the story of Mary Baxter and her love affair.

It was some time afterwards when I first heard about it. I met the friend who had sent Mary Baxter to me, and I asked, quite casually, for news of her.

"Haven't you heard?" said my friend. "Really, that girl gets the toughest deals."

I pricked up my ears. "Oh?" I returned. "I've heard nothing of her since she had her last consultation with me. What's the matter now?"

My friend told me what she knew. It was not much, and most of it was indirect. My interest was now fully aroused, and I found an excuse to get Mary Baxter to call upon me. She accepted my invitation with an alacrity I barely understood, though it was very flattering.

I had seen one Mary Baxter walk into my room, timid, self-abasing, fearful. I had seen another, some weeks later, go out self-assured, happy, and alive with hope. But the girl who was shown in to see me this third time was yet again another person. She was self-confident enough; but she was, for all that, afraid. Her fear was different now: it was fear of a problem she felt might prove too big for her, but it was not hopeless fear. She believed deep inside her that she could conquer her difficulties and get what she wanted.

She was genuinely glad to see me again, I think she wanted someone to confide in, someone who she knew from experience would not laugh at her, but try to understand the difficulties she was passing through. And indeed, in all conscience, it was a pitiful enough story that she told me. In truth, Fate's arrows had struck again—but this time they had found a target more resistant to their attack.

She had never been so happy in her life, she told me, as when she had looked in the glass and seen her face without that scar which had so long reproached her, and that crooked nose, which had seemed to mock her in her reflection. It had been as though an immense burden had been lifted from her, a burden whose real weight she had never fully realized till she was free of it. Now she was as light and free again as air. The past, with all its fears and doubts, was done with; and there was the future.

Though she had written often to James, she had not mentioned the operations. Anything might happen, and besides she had felt a little diffident. The old residue of shyness remained. It would be such a surprise for him when he returned. She wanted to keep it till then. Time went on, and there was no leave for the Army, then holding in the face of Rundstedt's last desperate counter offensive. A horrible idea came over her. Suppose James should never come back? Suppose he should be killed, and die thinking of her as scarred and disfigured? It was a terrible thought that made everything seem vain.

She might tell him, she decided. But words could not do it. He must be able to see her as she was now. No sooner had she reached her decision that she sought out one of the best portrait photographers in the West End. He had done her full justice. She brought a print with her, and it was a magnificent piece of work. Especially, he had caught that look of happiness and hope that had been in her eyes when I had seen her last. It is something photographers rarely achieve.

Then she had written a long letter, explaining all, so she told me, with a touch of her old self-abasement and fear, even her thoughts during all these years about her scars and what he must have thought of them, but putting it so that he could not fail to see that she never blamed him but understood.

"I was never much of a letter-writer," she said diffidently, "and I never knew I could write so much. But then," she added, "there was so much to say, I think I put the whole of myself into that letter." She sighed and a sad, distant expression came over her face.

She had sent it off. She had had small prints of the photographs made, because, she explained shyly, she had hoped he might carry them in his pocket wherever he went. Besides, it made them so much easier to send. And then she had waited anxiously for his reply. She was not afraid of what his answer would be. She was still convinced that her metamorphosis was what he had all along desired.

The days passed, and no letter came. But no news of him at all reached the village, and that gave her hope, though she dreaded the sight of the telegraph boy in the village street. After all, there was grim fighting out there in the Ardennes Bulge. No doubt he and many others had too much to do to write letters.

And then she heard that he was wounded. The news came as a shock to her. She felt numb and cold, not knowing what to do. For though she had imagined the worst, that he might be killed, she had never visualized him as being wounded. She wondered how serious it was. Would he be crippled for life? Was he badly hurt? Or—her hopes rose again—was it not much so that he would soon be right again, but posted in England, where she might see him?

Even though she thought she had imagined everything, she was not prepared for the truth. Walter Hoyle himself told her, with a grim terseness that overwhelmed her.

"News of James?" he said when she inquired of him. "Yes. Blind—blind for life."

He had shown no emotion. He spoke with an air of acceptance of Fate, as he might of the death of a prize bull in the herd . . .

All that day she had remained alone in her room. Her world had suddenly collapsed. James was blind! It was the most terrible of afflictions. Better that he had lost a leg, for then he might have an artificial one. But when the sight has gone, no skill can bring it back. He was condemned to darkness.

How glad she was then that she had sent those photographs. At least he had seen something of how she looked now and known that it had been all for him. He need not go about in his darkness thinking of her as ugly and repulsive.

Of course, she still loved him. Nothing now could tear her from him. He needed her as never before. Someone had to see him through life, for however well trained the blind may be there is a time when they need the help of others' eyes, and it is better when those eyes are loving ones. As soon as possible she must see him and talk to him.

It was not long before he was moved to a hospital near London. At the first opportunity she went to see him. He was in a wheeled chair on the terrace, enjoying the first sunshine of the spring—the spring that was a little later on to see victory. She sat beside him listening to his story, holding his hand, and feeling for the first time in her life that he needed her and loved her without anything in the way.

Like a thunderbolt from a clear sky the next blow came. He had been talking of how it happened, in plain matter-of-fact tones. After all, to him it was just one of the things that happened. His luck had been out, and another's had been in. That was all there was to it.

"I should have remembered that night anyway," he said. "You see, I had a letter from you."

It was the first time he had mentioned it. She looked at him expectantly.

"Yes. The posts were all to hell then, of course. You never knew when anything would turn up. Just my luck that they bunged the stuff in on us just as I was due out on a recce. One of those things again. I just put that letter in my pocket, and all the time I was out I thought of it and wondered, what you'd sent. It was a fat, interesting-looking sort of letter. Well," he added grimly, "I've gone on wondering. I never got the chance of looking at it, you see."

So he had never seen her photographs—never read what she had written. To him, she was still the scarred woman with the twisted nose, something ugly and abnormal.

"Of course, one of the nurses would have read it to me," he went on, "but somehow I didn't fancy them handling one of your letters. They always meant such a lot to me, darling. I've kept it on me ever since. Listen. I've an idea. Why don't you read it to me? That'd be grand."

He fumbled in his pocket and brought out the envelope. Her eyes filled with tears as she saw it. It was torn and dirty, but the flap was still fast.

She hesitated, took it reluctantly, and laid it on her lap.

"Aren't you going to read it to me?" he asked after a pause.

She choked back her sobs. "Not now, Jimmy dear. Some other time. I want to go on listening to your voice . . ."

He mused on, quite contented apparently at this refusal. And then she felt she wanted to scream in terror. It was too much to endure. Perhaps it was lucky the sister came along and told her she must go now. Visiting time was over. She could come again tomorrow.

"What am I to do?" she asked me. "How can I tell him now? I've staved it off and staved it off. Once he nearly broke my heart when he said he wanted to feel the scar on my face—the dear scar, as he called it." She choked, but controlled herself. "He thinks of me as I was then, and perhaps he thinks that after all it's not so terrible to marry someone who's scarred. If I'd been pretty he might think twice about it now. If I tell him, he'll think of me as someone he doesn't know—I won't be like the girl he remembers. But if I don't, it'll be living a lie to him, and oh! how can I do that? And then if I tell him or if someone else does, he may think I only want to marry him now out of pity. It's horrible, doctor. How I wish you could give me back my scar and my broken nose . . . What can I do?"

What could I say? There are some problems that one must work out for oneself, because they are in oneself, and it is a useless impertinence for others to presume to advise. I felt depressed that it was a Greek gift I had given her.

Yet I wonder: is it that? When I think of that look in her eyes, that look of courage which acknowledges difficulties but does not wilt before them, I have hope. If she has won through so much, shall the final prize escape her, that happiness she has sought so long?

III

THIRD TIME UNLUCKY

At parties, there is inevitably someone—usually a rather large and formless woman—who comes up and says: "Oh, Mr. Sava, I'm so glad to have met you. You know, I think it must be marvellous to be a surgeon. I mean, it's so *thrilling*". Well, perhaps it is, but not quite in the way the good lady means. After a while, in any event, one utterly ignores this sort of thing, for experience teaches that the same woman says precisely the same thing—with the necessary alteration to the word "surgeon" —to painters, musicians, and authors; to lawn-tennis players, politicians, and aviators.

To everyone there comes a time, I suppose, when he feels utterly discontented with his job and he wishes he were something else; but this is only normal human reaction and dislike of routine, the penalty, paid in terms of individual freedom, for civilization. But to the surgeon, particularly, there are moments when he wishes above all else to be anything but a surgeon. The whole world turns black to him. He doubts his skill and suspects his judgment. He may even, in his most despairing moments, utter the mental libel that the professional colleagues he consulted to confirm his own opinion are in a conspiracy against him and wish to bring him to obloquy and ruin by the shortest and quickest route. For there are cases on which one has lavished every possible thought and care, when one has the diagnosis and proposed treatment endorsed in consultation with the most eminent, when everything seems to be going right—and then the patient dies. No post-mortems, no heart-searchings, can find the cause of these disasters. They are, in our present state of knowledge, inexplicable. The tragedy in them is that a human life which by all the laws of probability should have been saved, is lost, and the reason cannot be found. There is not even the melancholy satisfaction of being able to profit by a mistake—for, so far as human analysis can see, no mistake has been made. Every surgeon has experience of such cases in his career, and each makes him feel that his energies would have been better expended on an occupation that involves no playing with human life —like playing the violin, or carving wooden dolls.

Of course, I do not mean that the choice is always between the two extremes of everything right and everything inexplicably wrong. Sometimes—and not infrequently—the unexpected happens, as it always must when so unpredictable an organism as the human being is concerned. But, more often than not, there is a chance to deal with this renewed challenge of Nature to the skill of man, and the threat of the unhappy ending can be crushed. Sometimes, the unpredictable happens to such an extent that the distracted surgeon might be forgiven if he imagined that dark, malignant forces were mystically working against him. These are the nightmares of a surgeon's life, even though they increase his proper sense of humility.

There was, for example, the case of Mrs. McIlroy. Here, indeed, the petty efforts of man became the sport of malicious gods. It was one that will ever remain vivid to me, for it was unique in my own experience, and it was the sort of thing that few surgeons can have the misfortune to know.

Mrs. McIlroy had come all the way from Scotland to consult me on the suggestion of a friend on whom I had, some time earlier, performed a successful abdominal operation. For some two years she had been in considerable and continual pain in the abdomen, which she had endured patiently. But it had defied all treatment, and at last she had—very wisely but by no means prematurely—decided that radical treatment was necessary. She was a pleasant woman in the early forties and was perfectly ready to fall in with anything I might suggest. She was, in fact, one of the most accommodating and cheerful patients I have ever had.

Thorough examination established what I had suspected from the start: she had a small growth in the womb, of a kind that is not particularly uncommon, and the only possible course was its excision. The operation is not perhaps the easiest and it has certain dangers attached to it; but those characteristics it shares with many others. In the overwhelming majority of cases it is completely successful, and there was no reason to believe that it would be otherwise in this particular case. I explained all this to Mrs. McIlroy.

"Yes, I quite understand," she said in that pleasant voice of hers. "Surely, one's always got to face a risk when one goes on the operating table, hasn't one? I'm quite ready to take it."

"I'm glad you take that view," I replied. "Nothing is infallible, though from the noise some people make when a doctor shows that he's not, anyone would be entitled to believe that we doctors were supermen possessed of godlike powers."

She laughed. "No, doctor. I don't believe that. But I do believe that I shall be in safe hands if you undertake it for me."

I thanked her, and it was decided that the operation should be performed at once—a course of which I thoroughly approved. This thing had been allowed to go on too long as it was. A few days later, therefore, she went into a nursing home. Nothing was then further from my thoughts than that this was going to be a case I was destined to remember as long as I live. There was not a single abnormal circumstance attached to it.

The operation presented no special difficulty, and I was thoroughly satisfied with it. There would be the usual period of anxiety during those critical immediately post-operative days, but then that was nothing out of the way. No operation runs exactly to schedule.

For the next two or three days, I had every reason to maintain my satisfaction. Her progress was, if anything, more rapid than the average, and her friends were already congratulating her. And then the first of the unpredictables turned up. Perhaps we had been too confident. I do not know.

Mrs. McIlroy, who had taken everything with the greatest calm and composure, suddenly began to complain that the pains were returning. They grew steadily worse, and I made a thorough re-examination of her. My thoughts grew troubled at what I found, but I did not say anything then. I insisted upon the necessity of another opinion, and I called in a physician, very well known to me, both professionally and personally, to confirm what I believed I had found.

There was no doubt about it. Mrs. McIlroy had started off by being a case in which I had no doubts whatsoever. Her symptoms were typical, and what I found when I actually performed the operation was equally characteristic. But now the strange imponderables of the human system were coming into play. The pains might be the same, or seem the same, to the patient, but the cause was very different. Mrs. McIlroy was presenting us with a very great rarity.

Her condition was, in fact, now very serious. A portion of the intestine had adhered to the womb, from which the growth had been excised. The result was a complete intestinal obstruction, and the only course open was to operate again. I explained this at some length to her and her relations, and they were all quite agreeable to my proceeding in any way that seemed best to me for the ultimate recovery of the patient. Weak and in pain though she was, Mrs. McIlroy was even prepared to make a jest of it.

"I feel quite proud of myself, Mr. Sava," she said. "You say my case is a great rarity. Perhaps I shall find immortality in the pages of some book you'll write on surgery."

That night I was again called to her bedside. The pains had redoubled and I could see at once that her case was now desperate. I gave instructions for the theatre to be prepared at once. There was no time to lose. I must operate at once.

The condition I had expected to find was there, but it was rather more complicated than either I or the physician had expected. Not only was there the adhesion of the intestine to the womb, but the actual intestine had twisted back on itself, so as to make a complete obstruction. The distance that separated Mrs. McIlroy from death was very short, and I had to work hard to make sure that she did not traverse it. Carefully I separated the adhesion, and then, no less delicately, I unwound the intestine and restored it to its normal condition.

Re-operating so soon on a patient, especially in abdominal cases, is always an anxious business, but she stood it well. She had in her something which the surgeon and physician by themselves cannot supply, though they can encourage it: the will and wish to live. At forty or so, she had many years in front of her, and she had found life, for all its ups and downs, enjoyable. I had sensed from the first that this was her attitude, and that whatever happened she would make a determined fight for life. But at that time I had not expected that her great courage would be so exactingly called upon.

I sighed with relief when, the operation over, she was taken from the theatre. It had been an anxious time, but the anaesthetist reported that she had stood up to it well, without the slightest suggestion of collapse.

For the next two days, the grim fight I knew she would make if asked, but which I never expected she would have to make, was waged. She had a blood transfusion, and we did all we could. But it was touch and go, and without her spirit I doubt if she would have survived. But once the dangerous stretch had been covered, she rallied wonderfully. Once again her friends congratulated her—and me—on her recovery. Ten days from the second operation, she was sitting up in bed. The course now looked all clear ahead, and even I was beginning to feel that another of Nature's scurvy tricks had been frustrated.

I wish I could end the case of Mrs. McIlroy there and show her returning cured to her Scottish home to resume that life that she found so good and for which she had so gallantly fought. I believed then that that was what would come in good time. She was no longer on the danger list—far from it. The stereotyped phrase of the bulletin: "Progressing favourably" was precisely correct as regards her condition, and the prognosis was good.

And then, on the twelfth day, the utterly unexpected happened. She complained of pain. It was the same pain as before, but this time it came on more suddenly.

When the news was reported to me over the telephone, I put all else aside and hastened to the nursing home. My examination made me very grave. Something of the same sort had occurred again. There was intestinal obstruction, and immediate action was demanded. But could it be done? We had operated twice. Could she stand a third visit to the table? Could we again defy the lightnings of Fate?

It was a serious matter, and I had to proceed with the utmost caution from all points of view. Mrs. McIlroy herself was in too much pain now to take part in a discussion, but I sent for her friends who had come to London with her and put the case to them bluntly. It was a million-to-one chance that this sort of thing should happen twice, I explained. The case itself was, so far as I knew, unique. And the odds that had to be accepted against success in a third operation were very long.

I met with every encouragement. For once, there was none ready to spring up and denounce the inefficiency of the medical profession in general and the circles of Harley Street in particular. Anyone to whom this suffering woman was dear might have been excused for thinking I had bungled somewhere, that I had not taken proper precautions or even that I did not know my job. But there was not a single word of criticism or doubt. I had their confidence. They were ready to accept any course I proposed as necessary.

It was a tribute that I shall long remember. In some small way it took off the natural sense of disappointment and even humiliation I felt over this affair. I knew, better perhaps than anyone, that there was nothing I had done or omitted to do of which I need feel ashamed. There had been no lack of precautions, no laxity in post-operative care. But the stark fact remained that I had operated twice on this patient and now she was in even worse case than she had been when she had come to me for consultation. It was a position I did not like, and I told these sympathetic people so.

"I am grateful to you," I said, "for the confidence you show in me. But I don't think it would be fair to you or to me that the responsibility of the next step should rest entirely on me. The risks to be accepted in a third operation of this kind are very great indeed. So far from minimizing them, I think it would be impossible to exaggerate them. The probability is that Mrs. McIlroy cannot stand the strain of another intervention. But the chance of success is there, and you agree with me that it should be taken. I suggest therefore that I should call in"—I named one of the most famous (and deservedly so) of contemporary British surgeons—"and ask him if he will operate. I shall act as his assistant. I know you trust me, but if we take this course you need have no reason to reproach yourself if the worst happens. You will know that the best skill in the country was employed."

Once more they agreed readily. They said that they did not consider it necessary from their point of view, that they would be quite content if I myself operated again, and they were sure Mrs. McIlroy herself would be, too. But they saw my point of view that the responsibility was too much for me to bear alone.

Their consent gained, I rushed to my car and set off to see the eminent surgeon. He smiled grimly when I put the facts to him.

"The penalty of fame," he said with gentle irony. "One is presented with other people's burdens and expected to carry them up the last and steepest hill." He smiled again. He is an ironic man with a mordant sense of humour. "Seriously, though, I'm interested, and I'm grateful to you for calling me in on a most unusual case. Yes, I'll operate."

I was thankful that he had accepted my arguments. I did not doubt Mrs. McIlroy's friends' protestations for a moment;

they were given in all sincerity. But if the end I dreaded came, doubts might arise. I was not concerned so much with the possible influence of a disaster on my reputation; it is a risk everyone must take, whatever his profession, at some time or another if his personal judgment is involved. I was genuinely anxious to see Mrs. McIlroy restored to full enjoyment of the life with which she was so much in love.

At that stage, I could hardly derive any satisfaction from the fact that I was intimately concerned with a case that, as the eminent surgeon had said, was "very unusual". The dark depression was already hanging over me. And as usual in this mood, I felt that my whole career had been purposeless, that the success I had won had flattered only to deceive. It is a curious frame of mind, this. One sees only that which lies before one's eyes. One's memory goes right out of focus. The cases in which one has battled for a life, regarded as hopeless, and won, might never have been. But the grim, inevitable list of fatal cases, the ones that every surgeon knows, assume an overwhelming importance.

Yet for all these obsessions in the moments of reflection, they all disappear when one resumes the task in hand. In the operating theatre the cloud lifts, here is another case before you. These are its problems, these its dangers. It is a job to be done—and no matter whether it is grave or slight, it has to be done to the best of one's ability. So it was that when I went into the theatre to assist the eminent surgeon who was to operate, the mood left me entirely. If I thought of the past it was only that we had achieved partial success twice; why should we not gain total success this third time? Is there not an adage that the third time is lucky?

The surgeon grunted softly when he had made his incision and revealed the abdominal cavity. There it was, almost exactly as before, except that this time there was no adhesion. The intestine had twisted back upon itself forming what looked like a knot that could not be unravelled. The stoppage was complete.

It was a long operation that would have tried the strength of a patient coming to the table for the first time; and this was the third occasion within a month. It was in that challenge to Mrs. McIlroy's strength and resiliency that the chief danger lay. But her reserves rallied gallantly. No warnings reached us from the anaesthetist, though of course all the means of rapid restorative treatment were at hand for use if that overtaxed heart should falter for a moment.

Deftly the surgeon did his work. At long last, he closed the incision. The third operation was over, and the issue of life and death had been fully joined.

Despite all our anxieties, for a week our hopes ran high. Danger never withdrew, but there were no signs of immediate collapse. That brave spirit fought back, determined not to let go of life while the faintest hope of retaining it remained. Nothing that could help her was left undone or unsupplied. Even I, oppressed again by the deepest doubts, began to allow myself the thought of recovery. It would indeed be a triumph if that desirable end was attained. But the major credit would be due to her.

But it was not to be. We had challenged destiny once too often. She had come to me a woman in great pain and even in some danger; and I had restored her. Once again, her evil genius had struck; and once again she had been plucked from the very jaws of death. But this third time was too much to ask, too much even to expect.

Mrs. McIlroy died, fighting almost to the last. Her unquenchable spirit passed quietly, and I believe without undue pain. The third time was unlucky, and she had gone, a victim of as remote a series of outside chances as could have been imagined. Indeed, they were beyond imagination.

Yes, it is cases like that which almost break the surgeon's heart. There is nothing to be learnt from them, except that which poets and philosophers, doctors and tailors, must take for granted: the infinite variety of Man. The surgeon learns that even the most minute descriptive book of anatomy cannot tell him precisely what he will find when he operates on a specific human being—a general picture, yes; but no more. His experience teaches him—and the physician, too

—that no two persons will behave alike in any given set of circumstances. There are those who have no wish to live—yet survive the most dangerous conditions. There are those, like Mrs. McIlroy, who fight to the last, yet neither their own determination nor the utmost skill can save them.

The infinite variety of Man! It shows in everything, even in the pattern of the pores on his skin. The cells in you do not behave precisely as the cells in me behave. Nothing is fixed, nothing certain.

It is just that infinite variety which urges me to set down these stories so that all may know surgery to be something different from the work of the engineer, whose resources enable him to cut girders and steel plates exactly like one another to within a thousandth of an inch or less, or turn out motor cars so that thousands are precisely alike. One sets out to write down the plain sory of an operation—and one ends up by portraying, however inadequately, a unique personality. And here I began a diatribe against the Fate that makes play of surgeons and I have come to making a salute of a brave and purposive woman. Her immortality will lie not in the dull pages of a textbook, as she prophesied, but in that eternity where the high spirits of those who loved life get their just reward and where the bolts of human uncertainty cannot reach her.

IV

"THOU SHALT NOT KILL"

I wonder who first made the *cliché* "brooding tragedy". It has always seemed to me a gross misstatement in the majority of cases. In the course of his work a doctor has a close-up view of a good many tragedies—the most pathetic tragedies of all, the tragedies of little lives, the frustration of the ordinary hopes and ambitions and loves of ordinary human beings, not the cataclysms that provide the material of the tragedies of literature and history. There are none to which that epithet "brooding" is less applicable. For these strike suddenly, without warning. They do not build up like thunderclouds in a summer sky. They are indeed those thunderbolts which Zeus used to hurl at mortal men for his sport and their good. One day life goes on as usual in its simple, unambitious way; the next hopes lie dead, the world has ceased to be. A cherished life has gone; the breadwinner who set out in the morning with a cheerful smile lies in some hospital ward and will never work again; the job that promised to last for a lifetime has vanished overnight—and the man is too old to get another except of the humblest kind.

It is life, I suppose—life with its fluctuations of good and bad. But it is difficult to contemplate it all with philosophic detachment. Every fresh encounter with it produces a new shock. The variety of suffering is as infinite as the variety of human personality itself.

I could see it in her eyes as soon as she came into my consulting-room. This, I said to myself, as I greeted her and made her comfortable in the armchair, is a woman who walks in the shadows of hell. One could see it in her eyes, which reveal everything from the petty lie to the depth of love; one could detect it in almost every little gesture with its overtone of weary hopelessness. One gets used to these signs, but that does not make them any the more welcome.

She had not come to see me about herself. She was perfectly fit and well, apart from the living doubt and horror in her mind. It was her son, her only son . . . I was her last hope, she explained with a burning tone of appeal that was almost irresistible, and if I failed her, the end of the world would come. Something of her own anguish of mind transmitted itself to me.

Tragedy? Yes; here was tragedy, one of the grim jokes of Fate that for all their horror have this saving grace: that they bring forth all that is noblest and most steadfast in the human spirit.

It had been a simple, yet a noble hope, when they had been married a few years before, a hope that, even in these days, inspires most married people. They wished to raise a family. They were deeply in love, these two who had not run into marriage on the first call of tumultuous youth, but had let their friendship ripen into lasting affection and hoped that it might reach full maturity in their children.

But, as so often happens with those who most desire children, none came. The years passed by, and still their hope remained unfulfilled. They looked with envy on their friends who had children, and the first grey shades of doubt and anxiety tinged their minds: was one of them not normal?

Two years had passed, two years of disappointment, and then the cloud of doubt had been dispersed. She found herself with child, and never was a woman more pleased. A load was lifted from her mind. She had always believed, even during that time of doubt, that one day the gift of the gods would be hers; and now her faith had proved justified. Her husband shared her pleasure.

Today there is a tendency—not so great as it was, but still quite marked—to look upon the pleasures of parenthood as a form of mawkish sentimentality, yet what greater joy is there, if one is honest, than this, the greatest fulfilment of the lives of men and women? And just because so many affect—whether from fear or from a mere desire to be "superior", I do not know—to despise parenthood, there is all the more delight in seeing people who do not disguise their happiness in it. These two, bound together by strong ties of affection, found their mutual experience deepened and enriched in a wonderful way.

And there was no hint of the tragedy in the cheerful way in which she went about her daily affairs. Those months of pregnancy were happy months; no dark cloud brooded over them. She would look into the future and see there the realization of the hopes she had so long shared with her husband, none the less real because they were simple, natural hopes, springing from the very nature of humanity.

The baby was born in a small nursing home; and again, over the event, no shadow of tragedy fell. Everything went well and normally. The attending doctor was fully satisfied. The calamity came with the child itself.

It had been born of love and of a passionate desire for parenthood. It was, if not a monster in the technical sense, at least so in the popular one. No crueller blow could have been struck at this devoted woman who had waited so long and so patiently for the fulfilment of her desires.

The baby was a boy. That is the statement of the plain physiological fact. But it was scarcely recognizable as a young human being. As a doctor one could be interested in it; as a man, one could only cry out against Nature for playing these unpredictable quirks and tricks.

There is a luckily rare condition of the human creature that is known as Mongolism. The name is descriptive for those victims of this horrible state have the slanting eyes that characterize the Mongol race—eyes that, in Western minds, have an appearance of the sinister and macabre. And Mongolism is indeed sinister. With the slanting eyes go an ugly snub nose, a mouth so small that it can barely accommodate the tongue, which, to make matters worse, is usually abnormally large. The cheek bones are high—a characteristic that increases the descriptiveness of the term Mongolism. Nor are all the deformities confined to the face.

The hands and feet are short and broad, and they are, too, unnaturally thick from back to front.

But these are by no means the worst features of this ghastly condition. Associated with it inevitably is idiocy. A Mongoloid rarely lives long, but however long he lingers in his painful existence, the brain does not grow. He is less than the four-footed creatures in the very things that make man different from them.

The little child showed all these appalling signs. More than that its head was hydrocephalic—a condition that, by itself, is terrible enough. Normally the brain floats, as it were, in a sea of cerebro-spinal fluid, which insulates it from shock. In hydrocephalus, there is an abnormal accumulation of this fluid. It fills the centricles or cavities in the brain, causing them to become abnormally expanded and thinning the vital membraneous skin of the brain itself. Such a brain, hampered by fluid and grossly distended by it, cannot even function properly, let alone develop. Hydrocephalus is a passport to death.

As if these afflictions were not enough, this unfortunate boy was also cursed with a cleft palate—that condition in which there is a gap in the roof of the mouth, and which is today almost always capable of surgical correction.

Specialists who examined the child at birth prognosticated an early death. Everything pointed to it, and the wonder was rather that such a deformed creature could come alive into the world. But prognosis, even with the surest guides, is always difficult; and this small boy, against whom nature seemed to have weighted the dice so heavily, showed as some sort of compensation, a remarkable tenacity of life. He refused to die and so justify medical opinion. And so far as his limitations permitted he developed well.

For that was the tragedy of it. Apart from these horrible deformities of mind and body he was a perfectly sound young human being in the physical sense. At twelve months, early death seemed even more a certainty; and the boy appeared even more determined not to die. Six months later, the state of affairs was the same. So he lingered on, with the door to death always open for him, though he steadfastly refused the invitation to enter.

A mother who had so passionately desired a child and had then given birth to one like this might have been excused if she had felt an intense revulsion of feeling and turned from it. But his mother did no such thing. I have rarely seen a more devoted mother. There was nothing she would not do for him; and at times one felt that, seeing him with the eyes of a mother, she regarded him as the most beautiful thing in the whole world.

But she did not spare her efforts to try to get some, at least, of his deformities corrected. She consulted specialist after specialist, but their opinion was unanimous: in the face of such a travesty of nature, medical science stood helpless.

Perhaps it was because unanimous medical opinion had already shown itself surprisingly wrong by expecting an early death for the boy, which did not occur, that she was so indomitable and persistent; she went from consultant to consultant, getting always the same, invariable reply: the case was hopeless. And so, in her unremitting search, she came to me . . .

I agreed to see the boy. A doctor must not have prejudices. Above all, he must always judge a case on its own merits and not let his mind be biased by what others have said before. That is the ideal at which he aims all the time in consulting work. Yet it is not always attainable. Few ideals are. She had mentioned some of the men she had seen before—names that commanded international respect. Was it likely that I could do anything when these men of eminence had declared themselves unable to help? It was more than improbable, but there was no harm in seeing the boy, even if it could do no more than bring this poor, tormented woman a little nearer to the truth that she still refused to admit: that her son must die, sooner or later. I think in her heart she knew it already, but the truth was too hard to bear and she clung desperately to a hope that, ultimately, she realized was a sham.

A day or two later she brought the boy. One glance at him was sufficient to see that his was really a hopeless case.

The Mongolism was typical, showing all the characteristics with an exactness that would have served the purposes of a textbook plate. And that grossly oversized head told its own tragic tale. Who could say how soon it would be before the pressure on the brain became too great and crushed out the life that should never have been?

But I made a thorough examination of him. The more I discovered, the more hopeless it appeared. I was ranging myself on the side of the others—not because of the weight of opinion that had already given its decision, but because one could not blink the facts. Of no-one was the old cynical adage that we start to die the moment we are born more pitifully true.

It was for this reason that I talked to the mother very earnestly. I told her quite frankly what my opinion was. The boy would die—whether sooner or later I could not say, for he had so far survived in an astonishing way, but die he would. However long he lasted, he would never be more than an idiot. . . .

"I don't care! That doesn't matter. He's my son, my child!" she returned with an intensity that amounted to fierceness. "I want him to live even if I feed him and nurse him till I die."

"There is something that is surgically possible," I went on, in a very doubtful voice.

She seized upon it at once. "What is it? Tell me. Please. No matter how little it is . . ."

She sprang to her feet, her face eager, but her eyes moist with tears at this faint ray of hope, which if I had been wiser I should perhaps not have shown her.

"It is surgically possible to correct the cleft palate," I replied. "But . . ."

"Oh, that would be something," she broke in. The happiness in her voice was unbearable, for I knew how false were the hopes I had unconsciously aroused. "It would be wonderful."

"I repeat," I went on, "it is *surgically* possible, but I do not advise it."

"Why—why?" She looked at me as though I was deliberately tantalizing her.

"Because I doubt if he would survive the operation," I said, as gently but as firmly as I knew how.

"But if there is one chance, doctor—one little chance . . ." She pleaded, she implored. It would be something saved from this tragic travesty of a human being. That, I believe, is what she thought. She saw one small score against Fate repaid.

I shook my head. "The chance is so small that it would be folly to take it," I said.

Again she broke into entreaties. I must do it—I must. It was my duty to the child—to humanity—to my profession . . .

No, it was not her impassioned eloquence that weakened my resolve, though, in her desperation, it was moving enough. Rather it was that as she talked a new picture crossed my mind. "My duty to humanity . . ." Yes, she put it like that. I tried to sweep the thought aside, but it persisted. Outwardly I checked her flow of words and spoke seriously.

"Have you ever considered having another child?" I asked.

She stared at me in surprise at this abrupt change in the subject. And then the most haunted fear I have ever seen looked out of her eyes. She almost cringed.

"No—no. I could never do that—never."

"But you do understand the scientific facts, don't you?" I persisted, that thought pounding in me all the time—the thought I wished to dismiss. "You know that there is not the slightest reason why—why this should happen again, every reason why it shouldn't. It's the one chance in perhaps ten thousand—perhaps the odds are longer . . ."

"Yes. Everyone has told me that." She shuddered. "But I dare not take even that risk. It would kill me if . . ." She broke off. There was no need to complete the sentence.

"It is a pity you think like that. Perhaps in time . . ."

"Never—never—never," she repeated insistently. It was the emphasis of panic.

And then, as abruptly as I had turned the discussion, she brought it back where she had left off. This time she cajoled me. The first fire of appeal had gone; what there was now was the pathetic pleading of despair.

"I will think it over, then. I will let you know in about a week," I said, at last. A little later, satisfied with that as best she might be, she left me.

No, I repeat, it was not her pleading, neither her fiery exhortations nor her broken appeals, that turned me and weakened me. It was that thought . . .

Alone, I could review the whole case more quietly. That highly charged emotional atmosphere had gone with her. Its only remnant was the memory of a mother fighting for something for her child, who was barely human at all. I dismissed even that picture from my mind. It was deeper than that. All sorts of side issues were involved.

The child must die. Of that, there could be no doubt whatsoever. He was doomed. If the very remote chance came off and he survived the operation for cleft palate, what good would it do? He would never have the brains to be able to speak properly. He would not speak with the tongues of angels; he would growl and mutter in the way of the beasts, less even than they. What value was his life?

And his life alone was not involved. She had shown it so clearly. She was brave, courageous, forcible, over this monster-child. But she was also slowly driving herself mad, whether she realized it or not. That fear which had possessed her when I mentioned the possibility of her having another child was hardly the fear of a person in full charge of her senses. Already those little premonitory signs of mental unbalance were appearing, and if they were allowed to grow . . . I almost shivered at the thought.

If it went on, it would mean the ruin of one whole, sane life for the cause of one misshapen and hopeless one. It would mean the break-up of a marriage that had obviously started in the happiest possible way. It would mean a load of suffering growing in geometrical progression.

She was fighting for the boy because he was her child, the child for which she and her husband had so ardently wished. Yes, that was true. Yet she was fighting for him also because she was afraid. He frightened her. She had given birth to this thing, and the shock had undermined her. Perhaps deep in her heart he revolted her, filled her with nausea. The fight was, in part, a reaction from those emotions. She wanted to show the world that she could and would fight for and love this, her son, no matter what he might look like.

Yes, that was the psychological background. It had already begun to dominate her whole life. If she had another child, the new one would turn her attention away from the boy while he lived. She would be deserting him, and the world would nod its gossiping head sagely and say "I told you so". It was that, more than the fear of conceiving another imbecile, that appalled and broke her. I was sure of it. And while this boy lived that fear would not merely remain but grow, grow—till she came to hate all humanity that was normal and healthy and happy.

While this boy lived . . . That was the crux of the whole matter. If the probabilities of science had won, he would have died almost at birth, and all this anguish of mind would have been spared. She might even have become so normal again that she would have ventured on a second trial of motherhood. The most venomous memories lose their poison in time. But while he lived, he was a constant reminder. No, more than that, he was building up ever fresh and greater mental problems.

The facts had to be faced. He was an idiot; and an idiot needed guarding all his life, whether long or short. True, he could be sent to a home, provided the parents renounced all rights, but this woman would never part from him like that. Protecting him, nursing him, had taken on for her the force of a holy crusade beyond the normal strength of motherhood.

My thoughts turned to the operation. The gap in the palate was large but not beyond the skill of man to repair. The operation involved was one with which, in my plastic work, I was not at all unfamiliar. But there were two points that stood out beyond that: two cardinal points. One was that the operation would serve no useful purpose; the other was that the patient would, so far as human powers of prognosis went, certainly die. More than that, he would probably die on the table.

It was at this point that my thoughts had arrived while she had been talking. From the larger aspect, was the operation useless? It would do no good to the boy, but for the mother? If he died, her grief would be deep and real; but after a time she would realize how great was the load that had been lifted from her shoulders. Little by little she would be able to resume the life of a normal person. The wounds in her mind would slowly heal. So, again, I asked myself the question: If he died . . .?

He must die in any case. It might be in weeks or even days; it might be in years; but the end of his life was foreseeable. Why should I trouble myself with disturbing thoughts? Simply because I saw that he had obviously, curiously strong powers of survival, and his life might be years—ten, twelve, perhaps. By that time she would be a wreck, with all hope of rehabilitation gone.

But my qualms were strong. I was proposing to myself a course of action that was, by the accepted standards, wrong. A life was a life, no matter how worthless it seemed to be, and it had to be saved. To think of accelerating its end was to run counter to all the accepted canons.

True, there were many who believed in euthanasia, among them some of the leaders of my profession. There were others —numerically more—who still clung to the old belief that in every circumstance life was sacred: except in war. If I took this course that was haunting my mind I faced big and terrifying risks.

Not long before there had been a case in which a coroner had been extremely caustic in his comments on a surgeon who had operated in a case which he knew to be hopeless. He was lucky to have avoided a charge of manslaughter. And here there were plenty of the highest medical witnesses who could, if they wished, come forward to say that I had taken a quite unjustifiable risk. For my concern for the mother would not count; that was only a vague opinion in the shadowy realms of psychology. The certainty of the boy's death under operation was as sure as modern science could make it.

Then, too, I had another and more personal problem to face. I was born into and brought up in the Roman Catholic faith; and though I am not, perhaps, among the most zealous of the Church's sons, the ideas of youth retain a strong hold on one's line of conduct. The Church admits surgical operations only to save life or ease suffering. The operation I thought of making would serve neither end. If the boy died, as he most surely would, I should ethically stand arraigned under the old Mosaic law: *Thou shalt not kill . . .*

Again the image of the overwrought mother came before me. *Thou shalt not kill . . .* But the boy might linger on and on, dragging his mother to the grave with him, breaking her in mind and body. If I did not operate, should I not be killing the mother, a more valuable life, one capable of yielding so much more to the world?

But the strict idea is that there is no relative value in lives. All life is sacred. One may weigh and compare ethical values, putting this against that, but in the long run there is the law to contend with. The law takes no account of such subtleties. You may kill a man with a knife or a bullet, and that is murder; you may kill him more slowly but no less surely by mental torture, and where then is the magistrate that will condemn you?

For a long time I fought with these conflicting problems. Now the vision of the boy in all his terrifying deformity came before me, now the image of his mother, looking at him with eyes that spoke less of love than of dedication. And each time I argued the matter afresh with myself, new points arose, new angles of approach, now swaying my mind this way, now that.

What should I do? What should I do?

I have just turned the pages of my appointments book. Six days ahead is an entry against half past four in the afternoon. It is the name of the woman. She will come for my decision. I wish I knew what was in her own secret heart. Would she, for all her heroic devotion, really like it to be all over at last? Does she really want this thing to live and burden her, blocking her every road to happiness? Yes, I wish I knew. It would make my decision so much easier. For even now I do not know what to say.

Thou shalt not kill . . . Yes. But whom?

V

HIS STRONG RIGHT ARM

The woman should not have been there at all. It was one of the most grimly busy nights we had had at the hospital during the whole of the blitz, and I sometimes wondered whether this stream of casualties would ever end. There were quite enough of them, poor, battered wrecks, to make the place unpleasantly full without the complication of relatives about asking questions and making protests. But they told me she would not leave her husband, and they had simply brought her along because it was the simplest way to avoid holding up the ambulance.

We want now to forget the blitz, though we must never forget its lessons. I mention it now, not because I want to tell another of those air-raid stories, but simply because in those conditions alone was this remarkable case possible. If I say "remarkable", I am not trying to make out that I worked a miracle. I think it was just part and parcel of the heightened sensibility, the greater awareness of everything, and the feeling that we must take the last ounce out of ourselves, that made it even cross my mind.

True, the woman had some slight injuries but nothing that should have brought her to a Class One hospital. The doctor at the First Aid Post could have dealt adequately with her. It was her determination that had brought her there; and I could see that nothing except brute force would drag her away from her man. I think she feared the worst with a vivid imagination. She could not afford to lose a single moment away from him.

If she thought that, I said to myself, as I examined her husband, her intuition is remarkably keen. He was a very bad case indeed. Idly I glanced at the label that the Civil

Defence people had tied on to him. "Hayward Bourne", it said, but the name conveyed nothing to me. I was not concerned with names and people at those moments. Perhaps I sometimes thought bitterly that I was not concerned even with surgery. There was just one ruling drive—save life at all costs; rob the Huns of their victims. It was patching and mending, cobbling as best we might. We had to act quickly without taking careful thought over procedures and alternative treatments.

His arm was the focus of my attention. Hayward Bourne would never use that arm again. Later, when I learnt the details of the case, I was told that it had been pinned beneath a pile of rubble that the Rescue party had lifted off fragment by fragment. It was so badly crushed that it hardly looked like an arm at all. Here and there one could recognize certain fragments of bone, but for the rest . . . There is no need to go into details. They are quite irrelevant for this story; and in any event we grew used to that sort of thing in those days.

There was, as I saw it then, only one thing to do. It must be amputated. The best I could do was perhaps to retain sufficient stump to enable him to have an artificial arm later —but even that was doubtful.

My house-surgeon was standing by myself. He was an intelligent young fellow who had worked intimately with me all through those terrible times, and he had got to that stage of understanding when it seemed he almost read my thoughts before I uttered them. No doubt, with the experience he had had, he had already formed the same opinion as I had: an amputation with all possible speed.

I forgot that the woman was standing so close to me all the time that she practically touched me. Her eyes were large and fearful and she turned them now on me and now on the form of her husband. The medical officer at the incident had given him morphine, perhaps the greatest blessing research has ever given to the suffering and pain-ridden.

I forgot her, I say, and turned to my house-surgeon.

"Bad case," I said. "It'll have to be amputated, of course. Get ready."

He nodded. My remarks were really unnecessary. He was merely waiting for the signal to begin.

And then Mrs. Bourne roused herself from that waking stupor in which she had appeared to be. She tugged violently, almost hysterically, at my arm.

"No, doctor, no," she exclaimed. "Please not that. Do anything—but give him back his arm."

I tried to shake her off, cursing the chance that had enabled her to be present. This was no time for discussion. His case alone was urgent enough; and there were many—too many—others. "Save his arm," she said. I wished I could. Every surgeon would want to do precisely that. But the thing was just outside practical possibility.

"There is nothing else to do," I said, without much politeness. "And it will not help him to discuss it."

She seized me and stood in my way as though she was determined she would rather stand by and see him die than let me perform the operation. There was a look of intense purpose on her face, which, in contrast to its expressionless pallor of a little while ago, was now alive and eager.

"He would rather die than lose his arm," she said breathlessly. "I know it. If that is all there is to do, then please let him die. I ask it, and I know it would be his own wish."

I stared at her in amazement. There was nothing hysterical or overwrought about her words. They formed a simple sincere statement based on utter conviction.

"But . . ." I began.

"Listen, doctor," she went on in the same forceful tone. "He is a violinist. No, I don't mean just another player of the violin. He plays superbly. Everyone says so, and that isn't just a wife's opinion. He lives for it. It means everything to him. It is his whole life and without his arm . . ." Her voice changed to impassioned pleading. "Please, doctor, save his arm! Take any risk you like if it gives just one chance in a million that he can use it again. Please, please!"

What could I say. To a violinist his right arm was his life

in every sense. But this was war, with all its horrors. Every day people were losing the things that were dearest and most precious to them. They were losing their lives, their homes, their loved ones. It was absurd to listen to such talk. No-one wanted to lose an arm or a leg. If there had been a chance of saving it, I would take that chance, as any of my colleagues would have done. None of us liked this scramble to save life and life alone.

So, at the most inappropriate time, I was brought up again by the old question that has always provided material for the arguments of philosophers and is a very real problem to doctors. Is saving life at any price the greatest service man can pay to man? Is life so sacred that it must be preserved, even if the thing we preserve is so battered that men may not look upon it without revulsion, and the man concerned has lost almost all the characteristics and functions of a human being except this thing we call, for want of a better name, life?

Pictures flashed through my mind in quick succession. I saw this man restored to life—but without his right arm. I saw him reading through the critiques of his early performances before this tragedy occurred. I saw him fondling with that remaining left hand the instrument that once has been his soul, perhaps plucking the strings softly and ineffectually. I knew nothing of him, it was true. He might be the most inept of gut scrapers. On the other hand he might be a product of that odd force in humanity which produces an Ysaye, a Kreisler, a Menuhin.

These things take some time to write, but they passed through my mind almost instantaneously in a series of vivid flashes in which every detail stood out clearly. And, as I saw these images, another thought insinuated itself. Could the arm be saved? Could it? And then, more insidiously, the doubt—why not?

It was early in the blitz. We had not then the lessons of war surgery that were to come to us from the blood-soaked deserts of North Africa. New methods were available, but many of us still doubted them. In common with all other

E.M.S. surgeons, I had studied them; though most of them I had heard of before.

There was the remarkable success of Professor Truetta in the Spanish Civil War. Perhaps it was the fact that he had recently arrived in this country to take up a research post at Oxford that brought his name first to mind. Yes, he had worked wonders. Would he have amputated this arm?

I looked again at the patient, while my house-surgeon, whom I had checked as he made to depart for his preparations, looked on wonderingly. It was a horrible case. But Truetta . . .?

Everyone knows of Truetta's method now. It has saved hundreds of lives in this war, and it has saved, also, those lives and bodies complete. The whole of the damaged member is encased in plaster of paris, and then it is left alone, for Nature to do the work herself. But then, especially in civil hospitals, it was almost unknown. But it was a chance—a remote chance.

I nodded to the woman.

"All right," I said thickly, "I'll see what I can do. But I make no promises."

She sprang towards me with cries of gratitude, but I brushed her roughly aside. Time, precious time that might mean lives, had been wasted enough already on this case. I was annoyed with myself for being a sentimental, easily influenced fool. The whole thing was madness. What hope was there that this fantastic decision of mine would be successful in the outcome? Practically none; I knew that. At the best, the arm would have to come off later, and probably the operation would be more difficult then. At the worst . . . But again my thoughts pulled me up. The "worst" in the conventional sense would be that Hayward Bourne, violinist of unknown capabilities, would die; but on his wife's showing that would be the best in his peculiar circumstances. Perhaps, after all, I was not quite so mad as my house-surgeon seemed to think I was.

I had given him revised instructions and he had looked at me as though I had taken very sudden and very complete leave of my senses. I had the passing feeling that his opinion of me had suddenly dropped, particularly in his view of my susceptibility to the pleas of distrait women.

It was not an easy job to reconstruct that arm as best we might and embed it in the plaster casing. It took longer than it should; I was using time that should have been spent on dealing with the other casualties who were still coming in. My conscience was reproaching me again. The whole thing was absurd. It must be a lesson to me not to be diverted from sound professional judgment by extraneous factors. Yet, for all that, I never felt that I was doing wrong. I was being rash, injudicious, idealistic if you like; but no feeling of guilt attached to it.

It was over at last. We had done our best, that young house-surgeon and I. And now there was nothing more to do, so far as that case was concerned, but hope for the best.

Until one grows accustomed to it, the Truetta method is very trying to the surgeon. In normal cases one has everything under observation. From day to day, one can see what is happening. Nothing need be taken on trust. One can search for the first faint indications of danger signals and find relief that there are none.

But when the wound is cased up in plaster, there are no such reassurances. X-ray photographs are possible, but they do not tell one all one wants to know. There is nothing, even today, which is a complete substitute for first-hand examination. Everything has now to be a matter of faith. There is the temptation to strip off the cast too soon, just to see that all is well; and it must be resisted at all costs, for that is the sure way to disaster. Without the balm of daily close examination one watches anxious for the secondary symptoms of gangrene.

There were none, so far as I could see. We watched the case carefully,—some said with too much care, for there had been one or two unpleasant comments on the way in which I had dealt with this case. And then the moment came for the plaster to be removed.

It was a time of great anxiety. Up to that moment, I

had itched all along to get that mask away so that I could see what was happening and learn how far our hopes were justified. But now the actual time had come I felt myself reluctant and unwilling to take it off. I feared what I might find. More and more I became convinced that the upshot would be a tragic commentary on the folly of those who abandon the safe paths and on the adage that pride goeth before a fall. I could see, in my mind's eye, the faint flicker of a smile on my house-surgeon's face when I gave him instructions to get the theatre ready for an amputation, and the haughty superiority of the theatre sister.

It was a critical and tormenting experience, but it had to be done. Carefully I examined the arm, and then slowly I raised my head and looked into the bright, ecstatic face of my house-surgeon. For it had come off, that extremely long shot. We had saved not merely a life, but an arm—which looks like an inversion of values but is not really, for to save a life is a great thing, but to save that life with all its potentialities unimpaired is a greater, whatever the circumstances. And here, I believed, though on the flimsiest reasons, that the unimpaired faculties meant more to this man than the simple fact of life.

It was triumph enough. But it was not the end. True, the arm was whole again. But how far would he be able to use it? Would he regain all his old skill, or would this limb be little more than an artificial one with which to manipulate, a little clumsily, the tools of everyday existence, like a knife and fork, a pencil?

The progress of the case was fair but slow. He had to re-educate those torn and crushed muscles and nerves which he had formerly trained to such co-ordination—for even the least skilful of musicians requires an extraordinary degree of muscular co-ordination. In an adult this re-education is by no means an easy matter, especially as the sufferer is apt to get impatient and discouraged that he cannot do at once what before he did so easily and naturally.

Even when, at last, I discharged him, thinking that now no-one could help him but himself, I was filled with doubt.

That arm was so reluctant and sluggish. He said once that it was like an arm of lead. And of what use is an arm of lead to a violinist? It would, indeed, be a grim irony if, having gone so far, having succeeded in an outrageous game of chance, the final result should be a partial crippling worse even than complete loss of the limb.

I lost sight of him after his discharge from treatment. Occasionally I thought of him and wondered how he was getting on. None of my musical friends could tell me anything of Hayward Bourne, a Canadian violinist. They would shrug their shoulders in that superior way which is so typical of the musical *cognoscenti*. "There are so many fiddlers," they would say. "Canadian? I expect he plays in a dance-band or something like that." Hayward Bourne seemed to have vanished.

I was rather annoyed at this flat ending. His wife, overflowing with gratitude, had promised to keep me posted of his progress, but I had heard not a word from her. Perhaps, after all, it was a failure, and they had returned to Canada to find some obscure living. It was, I felt, a rather shabby return for all the time and trouble I had spent on that case—time and trouble I should have saved but for yielding to Mrs. Bourne's urgent pleas and, probably, a sentimental regard for all who live for art.

It was several months later when news came to me. I returned from lunch late one day and was told that a man and woman were waiting to see me. Their name was Bourne . . . the man was an old patient. They would not take much of my time and begged that I would see them, though they had no appointment.

"Show them in," I said. "I think they're people I want to hear from."

As soon as they entered the consulting-room, my eyes strayed to the man's arm. In his neat jacket, it looked well enough and he did not wince when I gripped his hand but, instead, returned my intentionally ferocious grasp with interest. That was reassuring enough; but even more exciting was the look of happiness on the faces of both of them.

Mrs. Bourne seized my hands in hers.

"Oh, doctor," she cried. "How can we ever thank you! He's well and fit again and playing as perfectly as ever. He's just starting on the tour he came over here to make."

I expressed my pleasure. I was glad of it. And he told me how difficult it had been.

"Worse than learning," he explained. "Much worse. You see, I could still do everything with my left hand. But my right was practically useless. I could finger any sort of passage, but I couldn't bow it, no matter how simple it was. I nearly gave up, and that almost broke Joyce's heart. But I managed to keep on. Then the miracle happened. I suddenly found the old skill coming back of its own, and once it began it came with a rush. It was a miracle."

"You seem cut out for miracles," I commented. "It was a miracle your wife was with you that night—otherwise you would have no arm at all. It was another miracle that the chance we took came off. Frankly I never expected it to."

"We owe everything to you," said Mrs. Bourne. "But we're wasting your time. We had to call to thank you. It's all so truly wonderful."

"I'm very glad to see you," I replied. "I've often wondered how things were going, and now I know. It couldn't be better. Why didn't you write to me or telephone me, as you promised, Mrs. Bourne?"

"I wanted to wait till he was completely recovered," she answered. "You see, I never doubted that he would get all right one day. You had saved his arm and God would not be so unjust as to leave it at that."

"I wish I had shared your faith," I observed with a little grimness.

They said goodbye effusively, and I was a little glad to be rid of their garrulous gratitude. And as they were leaving they invited me to go to one of his forthcoming concerts, at a club for Canadian troops in London. Mrs. Bourne thrust a paper into my hand as she left, but absently I put it in my pocket.

So I could add the case to my list of undeserved successes, I thought. That is always the way. One takes an outside chance and if it is successful one is acclaimed as a past master. One performs the most difficult operation, using every ounce of skill one possesses, and one gets no more than a cheque and a slip with the formal words "With compliments". Perhaps it is better so. A surgeon who gets a reputation as a miracle worker is already on the road to disrepute.

A day or two later I wanted an odd scrap of paper for a note, and feeling in my pocket drew out the piece Mrs. Bourne had given me. I glanced at it, and my eyes opened. I do not know what I had expected, but this, surely, was anticlimax. I had missed the concert, of which this bill gave details, and I had to confess to myself that I was glad I had. For it was "popular" in the worst possible sense. There were the names of comedians known to me to have little wit other than the easy type of salacity. And mixed up with them was the name "Hayward Bourne and his violin".

I laughed outright. It was really too absurd. I had taken all that trouble, thinking I was saving an artist's art, and now, when it was all over and success had been won, it appeared that he was a minor variety act. Perhaps that right arm I had restored was used for producing ukelele effects on the violin or sliding the bow up and down to imitate the sound of hens . . .

This was the final touch of irony. No wonder, I thought, he found his recovery so rapid! His standards were those of the trick cyclist. So long as he could astound he did not care. And the wonderful ideas I had cherished of having given back an arm that excelled in subtlety and delicacy were the sort of moonshine out of which all fantastic dreams are made. I did not regret having saved a human being for his vocation, but I took sudden resentment for that air of conviction with which Mrs. Bourne had almost bludgeoned me into taking the course I did, perhaps at the cost of suffering to the other waiting casualties. It must show me once for all never to change my mind once I had honestly made it up.

A few months ago I went to a concert given in aid of the Red Cross. There was a famous orchestra and a bunch of distinguished soloists, but I went hurriedly, and, being with friends, did not even trouble to glance at the programme. It was a concert of familiar music suited to the taste of an audience that came primarily for reasons of charity and social prestige.

There was one musical friend in my party, a man who listened to most of the first half of the programme with an air of haughty superiority. During the interval, just before the second half commenced, he turned to me and tapped his programme.

"This should be interesting," he said. "The Beethoven Violin Concerto. They tell me this fellow is a very remarkable player. Had wonderful notices lately. A Canadian, so I understand."

"A Canadian?" I returned. "What is his name?"

"Hayward Bourne and . . ."

But at that moment the leader of the orchestra came in and the applause began. He was followed by the famous conductor leading the soloist.

No, there was no doubt about it. It was my casualty case. He looked in perfect possession of himself and acknowledged the applause with restrained dignity.

My mind was in a whirl. What was he doing here? I had thought he was a variety turn, a maker of farmyard noises . . .

But I had little time to pursue my thoughts. The conductor poised his baton and a hush fell on the great hall. The music began. And as I listened, I knew that Hayward Bourne was indeed an artist. His tone was glorious—and I know enough about violin playing to recognize that the secret of tone lies almost entirely in the cunning of the bow hand—the right hand.

So my work had not been in vain. It had been in truth an artist's arm I had saved. The memory of my doubts and scorn returned on me in a flood, as the spell of the music broken at last, the wild applause burst forth. I laughed openly. And my musical friend shot at me a glance that only made me laugh the more.

VI

SHALL DANCE AGAIN

There is one other story of the blitz I must tell, not because I wish to revive memories of that appalling experience of so many, but because it was a case that arose out of the blitz and, in the circumstances, could not have occurred but for conditions as they were. Perhaps it has much the same moral as the case of the violinist. I do not know. I am not seeking morals and trying to point my tales with a philosophic tag.

Yes, during those days we took risks from which otherwise we might have shrunk. Our lives were in our hands night after night. What did one risk more or less matter? But there must be a limit to risks. To the surgeon probably the most difficult question of all is that oldest of all: what risk is justifiable and what unjustifiable? The balance sways from case to case. The risk of yesterday becomes less than that today, and a normal procedure of tomorrow. It is one of those things in which the last court of appeal is one's own personal judgment based on the evidence available. Another man's may well be different, but there is none who can with certainty say which is fundamentally right. And in this case there is another element of controversy: How far are the bodies of the dead sacred? Shall they be used to save another life?

This is delicate ground because it cuts across all manner of religious and ethical principles. It is not something that can be decided by scientific method. And because of that it is one of those things which give the lie to those who say the world can be run by science. For in the background of every human problem is the question of right and wrong—the question of ethics. The scientist's test is, will it work?—

does it provide a guide to future action? It cannot say, even when it gives an affirmative answer to these questions, whether the course proposed is the one that accords with moral principles—and on those, even in a country like England, there are deep and unbridgeable gulfs between opinions.

It is a question that will have to be thrashed out soon, for as science progresses, new and startling techniques are being made available to the surgeon. He knows that by making grafts from recently dead bodies, he can achieve certain results. In Russia, the blood from bodies has been used to form a central reserve for blood-transfusions. With each new discovery on these lines, the question becomes more urgent.

In the past life has been held sacred, and it has been the practice to stop at nothing in order to save it. But these new methods cut across that outlook to some extent. Is a life bought at the price of robbing the dead, as some put it, anything but a sham, a mockery?

Superstitions die hard, and all our science has not succeeded in brushing away the last dusty cobwebs. And one of the superstitions that lingers most obstinately is the mystical respect and veneration of the cadaver. We may have advanced far from that rigid point of view which made it difficult to obtain bodies for the purposes of experimental dissection; but even so, there are many who regard any sort of intervention on a dead body as a form of sacrilege, not merely damning the doer but also in some mysterious way debasing the beneficiary. Even cremation has had a hard fight for recognition as a scientific means of disposing of the dead, and some churches still forbid it.

As soon as one begins to make use of techniques that involve graftings from dead bodies, one comes across a tangle of confusing ideas, some pure superstitions, some ideals honestly and sincerely held (and therefore to be respected), and yet others plain muddleheadedness.

In conditions of extreme urgency, such as those of the battlefield or during the blitz—which was a battlefield—things are sometimes done which one would not attempt in more normal conditions. One would think about them, consider them from various angles, and probably give way to doubts which weakened the power of action. When emergency is the spur, there is no room for doubt. One makes up one's mind—and action follows.

So it was with the case I have now in mind. It was another of those nights when too much attention was being paid to the district in which my E.M.S. hospital was situated. The casualties were not many, but they came in a steady trickle. There was time for thought, for doing a little bit more than the minimum necessary to save life, which is all that could be expected of anyone when there was a bad local incident and serious casualties poured in, swamping the resources available. I was busy but not pressed. I could take stock of each case and weigh it up. I could sometimes employ procedures that, in heavier conditions, I would not have attempted because of the time involved—time that might mean the difference between life and death to one of those waiting outside.

My casualty was only a young girl. Her face, even then, had a certain tranquil beauty, and I noticed the extreme shapeliness of her limbs and body. But it seemed as though something of that physical symmetry would be lost—thanks to the devilries of the Luftwaffe. Her right leg was in a terrible condition. It had not been crushed, but it was lacerated throughout its length. Ugly edges of bomb splinters could be seen in it.

Yes, it was an ugly case, but I had dealt with these before. Every one of us in the hospital had. No doubt I could save the leg, give it back something of its form. But that would be all. I knew that the leg would be useless thereafter, a mere prop. The nerves were torn and broken and some would have to be cut out. That leg when it was dealt with would be like a factory from which the machines have been removed—a shell that no longer housed its proper activities.

She was delirious when brought to me. Often what she said was quite unintelligible, but there was one refrain that ran through it all.

"My leg," she muttered. "Oh, my leg. It's my leg." And she said it with a curious emphasis as though it had some very special significance. And then with that curious access of lucidity that so often comes in cases like this, she opened her eyes—I noticed they were a deep violet blue—and looked straight at me.

"Shall I ever be able to dance again?" she asked in a normal voice, as though asking whether she should take an umbrella with her on a walk. "Of course I shall. It's *Swan Lake* next week. You'll put it right for then, won't you?"

She fell to muttering again, and I listened more intently. Yes, it was more intelligible now: all this gibberish was ballet talk, that strange Franco-Italo-Russian which makes the international vocabulary of the dance today. She counted a few steps in very English Russian, and a sudden nostalgia rose in me. Here, in the middle of the London blitz, the Russian numerals were the last thing I expected to hear from the lips of a wounded English girl. The names of ballets kept recurring—*Sylphides*, *Giselle*, *Swan Lake:* she knew her classical repertoire then. And ballet terms came in a flow, as though she was memorizing some movement. She muttered of *entrechats* and *fouettes*, of *tours en l'air* and *arabesques* . . . The mind plays odd tricks. I am Russian, and as was usual for one of my particular section of society I had been brought up on the ballet, which is forever dear to me. In the course of a few seconds I thought of the great ones I had seen, of the Maryinsky Theatre in Petersburg, the Opera House at Kiev. All my Russian love for the ballet flowed over to this poor girl. She adored it, too. It was her life. And the hounds of Hitler had robbed her of her leg.

My mind worked on. There had been *The Nutcracker* I had seen in Moscow . . . I had the curious illusion that that was the place to which all my thoughts had been trending. Moscow! Yes it shared with Petersburg the distinction of being the mine from which the greatest gems of ballet had been drawn. It was the capital of a new Russia now, a Russia different, stronger, happier, than any I had known in my youth, a Russia that was not afraid to do bold things and to carry forward the standard of mankind.

It was in Moscow, at one of their great medical research centres, that a team of surgeons had experimented with the grafting of nerves from dead bodies to take the place of those missing from live ones. And the technique had proved successful, at first fitfully, but later with increasing regularity.

Nerves so grafted do not remain in the body to which they are transplanted. The recipient cannot say that he has so-and-so's cast-off nerve in his leg or arm. What happens is that the dead nerve is joined between the ends of the living one, so that it closes the gap. The nerve uses this as a bridge and gradually grows across it so that eventually the ends are joined. The secret of success lay in having available nerve tissue from a freshly dead body.

I looked at this child still muttering of her ballets and thought swiftly. Could it be done? It was a wild, fantastic thought, but it could not be denied. Here was a chance to make an important experiment and also perhaps to win back happiness as well as life for this girl.

I needed fresh nerve tissue. It was as though the Fates were tempting me. There had been at least one fatality that night. A young man had died on the table. The surgeon—it had not been I—had made a brave and brilliant effort to save a life that was forfeit from the moment it came into the hospital. There was just a slender chance. The surgeon took it, and failed. But no man could have succeeded where he had not.

Everything was there. The will and the wish; the knowledge—for I had studied this procedure in some detail; and the material—all were waiting. It had to be done.

I told my house-surgeon what I wanted, and his eyes grew wide with astonishment. But there was no reluctance on his part. He was young and enthusiastic, and to youth the mere fact of novelty has an appeal of its own. A technique, because it is new, has in their eyes a much greater value than an established one, used since the time of their grandfathers or before. He felt he was going to take part in a very interesting experience and was glad of the opportunity.

To some, what followed may seem more like ghoul's work than surgery. Carefully we dissected a good twelve inches of the nerve tissue from the leg of the young man who had died. And then followed the work of grafting. I had operated on the girl before, extracting the embedded splinters and doing everything I could to preserve the shape of the leg. How lucky it was I had time for all these refinements. There were times when one felt like weeping at the roughness of the methods one was forced to use.

Making that graft was no easy matter. It is a difficult enough job when one is familiar with the technique and conditions were ideal. But I was making use of a technique that was to all intents and purposes entirely new to me, and conditions were far from ideal. There had not been time to think over the actual procedure, nor had all the preparations been made that I should like to have seen made. But we did our best, and at last it was finished.

I sighed as I put in the last stitch to the wound. It had been a more ticklish job than I had expected, and the issue was very much in doubt. But it was done. For good or ill it had been done. I was satisfied. I had obeyed a curious prompting within me, and though I do not believe in "hunches", I felt that it had been the right thing to do.

There followed the long period of waiting and watching and wondering. I gave to that case every minute I could spare. I was desperately anxious that it should succeed, not only because I wished to restore, if I could, this girl to the life she loved, but also because I might need the knowledge in the future.

As she grew better and stronger, she was always asking about her leg. Would she be able to dance again? And if so, when?

I had to tell her frankly that I did not know the answers to these questions. Time alone could show, and with that she had to be content. But she was glad to find someone who could talk ballet to her, and often when I could make the time I would go to see her just for that. It cheered her and comforted her. She was happy now, because she had hope.

It had been different with her mother. I had talked to her very seriously, told her the facts of the case, and outlined what I had done. She was frankly appalled.

"But, doctor, I would never have consented to such a course!" she exclaimed in a shocked voice. "I hardly know what to say about it. The idea is revolting to me. Do you think it wise to tell Pearl?"

"Certainly I do," I replied. "I myself don't share your qualms, or I should never have acted as I did. There was the chance and the opportunity, and I took both. So far, no-one is more pleased with the results than I am. It is essential, I think, that your daughter should know the truth. There is nothing revolting about it. All I have done is to transfer the tissue of one human body to another—and even then, the grafted tissue won't remain. You see, unless she knows all this, she may be tempted to expect too much and strain the leg by trying to dance too early."

"I am sure she will be as shocked as I am," persisted the mother.

"Why?" I returned. "Young people have as a rule very different ideas on these things from their parents, you know. And I rather imagine that to Pearl her dancing is everything. She would rather have the chance of dancing again as things are than be a helpless semi-cripple with only one sound leg."

"I hope you're right, doctor," said the mother doubtfully. "I still look on the whole thing with a sort of disgust—though, of course," she added quickly, "I know you acted from the best possible motives, and that you worked for the best. I'm grateful to you for that. I only wish there could have been some other way."

"Look at it this way," I replied. "Would you rather see your daughter walking about like a normal human being—leave out the dancing for the moment—or would you like to see her limping about?"

"Of course, there's only one answer to that, doctor. You know that. But even so . . ."

"Then just imagine she's had some very obnoxious medicine," I persisted. "You might be disgusted at some of the things we doctors prescribe sometimes, you know."

"I can believe that. But I wish it could have been something else than part of a dead man's body."

There I had to leave it. She would not be budged from her ideas. She was more than grateful for what I had done—especially when the girl began to walk—but she could not reconcile herself to the method employed.

It was by no means the same with Pearl. Not only did she show no signs of aversion from the technique I had employed; she asked for more details. She had a lively and inquiring mind, and I think the fact that she had been the subject of this unusual experiment gratified her and made her feel that she had something better than others.

Yet though she discussed her operation with me, it was always ballet she came back to. She was delighted when, with support on either hand, she made her first faltering steps. And as she grew stronger, so her hopes rose. Now it was not, for her, whether she would dance again, but when.

Her progress produced a very different reaction in me. I could see dangers looming up. Dancing—ballet dancing—and walking are two different things. The muscles are employed quite differently, and the ballet dancer has to develop muscles which are very little used by the ordinary human being. Pearl, having advanced so far, felt that the rest would follow automatically. What I dreaded now was the shock that must follow if she should be disappointed. In some ways that might even be more disastrous than the original accident.

When, at long last, I gave a grudging assent to her trying a little dancing, I made a point of learning the name of her teacher. Luckily, the teacher was one well known for her soundness. I went and saw this lady and told her all about the case. I found her sympathetic and most understanding.

The modern dance teacher has an extraordinarily fine knowledge of practical anatomy and muscle-training, and this one was even above the average. I felt when I left that I could trust her implicitly, and that she would not hesitate to tell Pearl if her hopes were ill founded.

So the case passed from my hands, one that I shall long remember for the curious way it came about. But I got a report from the teacher a little while after, saying that Pearl was able to do a few simple exercises at the barre.

It had been a success, but the full measure of that success was not revealed till a little while ago, when I went to a performance by one of the smaller British companies. The name of one of the minor soloists was Pearl Hillier. She was certainly competent, though the dance itself was not exacting. I studied her closely. No, she would never be a Pavlova. But then would she ever have been? And when, urged by a sudden impulse, I went round to the back of the stage afterwards and talked to her I discovered something that brought as much satisfaction and pleasure to me as if I had assisted at the birth of a new star.

She knew that stardom was not for her. But she was happy—happy in being able to do, however humbly, what above all else she wanted to do. She was whole. And she knew she might so easily have been a patched-up wreck, filled with thwarted ambitions she could never realize.

So we come back to the question: Is this happy life a greater thing than the twelve inches of nerve tissue from a dead man's body?

I think it is.

VII

THE OTHER SIDE OF THE COUNTER

It is only in moments of relaxation that a surgeon can allow himself to think about his patients as human beings. While he is operating, even when he is examining them, he must exclude all irrelevant thoughts from his mind. Though it may be his closest friend who lies on the table before him, it must not be permitted to influence him—at least consciously, though there may be, in such circumstances, an unconscious urge to do even better than one's best, an urge that may be dangerous because it may lead to over-anxiety. Of course, it is important to know quite a lot about one's patients; often the smallest personal detail of their lives can be of the greatest help. But in the strictly professional capacity a patient is a patient. In the consulting room he is a piece of human machinery that has broken down and the cause of the breakdown must be discovered; in the operating theatre the only thing of importance is to repair and restore the faulty mechanism.

In those moments of relaxation, however, he can allow his thoughts to take their own course. Often, he wonders what it is like to be on the other side of the counter—to be a patient instead of a doctor. This does not mean that members of the medical profession are never ill and therefore never have treatment. But even if one undergoes an operation oneself, one cannot quite become as an ordinary, non-medical patient. One knows what is going to happen. One knows the risk involved. One is not stepping into the unknown as the average man or woman is on entering hospital or nursing home. A known risk, an appraised ordeal—either is easier to bear, no matter how great it may be, than the unknown.

There is very little to go on. Patients come back after the operation and express all sorts of emotions from gratitude to abuse. They may be delighted or disappointed. They may see a miracle in the simplest recovery or fail to admit that the miracle they expected is an impossibility. Their whole point of view is different. Their chief interest is in the result, not in what went to make it, and they are reluctant, even under pressure, to describe their feelings and experiences, except in the most general terms, which are coloured by their final reaction. For if the operation has not yielded the results they optimistically and in spite of warnings expected, their descriptions are sombre; their whole attitude is one of "have we, then, suffered so much for so little?" And if the operation has been a complete success, then everything has been wonderful.

The only thing to do, as a rule, is to guess—and guessing is easy travel often to the wrong destination. One may dramatize one's patients or, in moments of expansion, sentimentalize over them. One may see only their unreasonableness or marvel at their gratitude. One may even wonder sometimes whether that very gratitude is really sincere—though that is an unworthy thought and only comes in those black moments all of us know when it is so much easier to think the worst of everything and everybody.

Not long ago, I received a document that is of supreme interest to me because it is a real and earnest attempt to analyse and describe feelings from the first moment of consultation to the final interview. For the first time, on reading this, I felt that at last I had spent a few moments on the other side of the counter and understood a little more than I had ever done. But let me start at the beginning.

She was a Scotch girl. Let us call her Jean Grant. She came to me out of the blue—the blue being the tasteful uniform worn by the postmen of the General Post Office. It was just one of many letters, asking for an appointment, with no introduction from a doctor or a friend. She had read my book on plastic surgery and believed I could help her.

I sent her a reply in the normal course and made an appointment for the following week.

She had told me of her trouble when she had written to me—hypertrophy of the breasts;—but I had not been prepared quite for the degree of enlargement that she suffered from. Her bosom was enormous, and when she told me that she was suffering acutely from inferiority feelings, I was not at all surprised. For a young woman in her twenties, they must have been something more than embarrassment. The thought of that disfiguration must have coloured all her thoughts, even made her shrink from the companionship of her fellow beings. Her whole manner as she entered my room showed that.

I examined her carefully. Operations to reduce outsized breasts are, of course, not uncommon in plastic work, but they are not quite so simple as some seem to imagine. There are quite a number of factors to bear in mind. It is, for example, not much use to reduce the size of the organs, but leave the patients with scars which, even if they do not show in the ordinary way, are nevertheless disfigurements. And above all, especially in a young woman, the operation must be carried out in such a way that the physiological function is not impaired. This is an important point that must be observed in all plastic operations. The purely cosmetic aspect must never be allowed to obscure the other considerations. No surgeon should lend his skill to a procedure that, while it may restore human symmetry or even create it where it did not exist before, results in the loss of some vital function of the body.

The problem of scars is one of technique. By the use of methods which I have developed, it is possible in most operable cases to reduce the scars to one on each side—and each of these is hidden in the armpit. Even these are inconspicuous, if one employs the subcutaneous suture. The question of preserving physiological function depends to a very large extent upon the conditions of each individual case, and is a matter on which the most careful judgment must be made.

My decision on this particular case was that the breasts could be very considerably reduced and that the results would be satisfactory. The girl looked at me as though I was giving her a reprieve from death. There was no reluctance about her. I advised her to think it over, but she was all for immediate action. Perhaps she had suffered psychological torments for so long that the very idea of a moment's unnecessary delay was almost intolerable to her.

I will not tell the rest of the story in my own words. Let me leave it to her, for it was she who sent me the document I mentioned earlier that gives me an insight into a patient's mind. Yes, I asked her for it, because she seemed the sort of girl who could give me what I had so long been seeking. She had the right kind of mind. Her war job was research of some kind; she had a scientific training and outlook; but also she was a human being, with the ability to live and feel and not just to look on existence and people as merely the raw material for dry-as-dust dissection and analysis.

Here, then, is her story. If it repeats something of what I have already said, there is at least this difference: that I have put down the details of the case as I saw them in a professional way; she has described them as she experienced them and as they formed part of her life.

The abnormality from which I suffered such intense embarrassment, both physically and psychologically, was considerably over-sized breasts. Written in black and white on paper, that may not look so crushingly terrible, but the perpetual consciousness of this condition for eight or nine years insidiously produced a very real inferiority complex. I felt self-conscious always amongst other people; I had practically given up sports such as swimming and diving, which, before I became mature, had been amongst my great activities; and naturally enough all thoughts of possible marriage in the future were warped by the insistent tremor of inferiority. I railed against the destiny which ordained that I should be thus handicapped in a life that was otherwise exceptionally healthy and active. Life was indeed overcast, and though I did my best to view things rationally and with common sense, I felt always that I was stigmatized.

In the course of general reading, I had looked through a number of medical books, though I had never found anything which dealt with my particular abnormality. One day, however, I happened upon a book by George Sava; and taking it home with me, I became absorbed in the different applications of plastic surgery. At three o'clock in the morning I reached the chapter which startled me beyond measure and which led to the operations which proved to be a turning point in my life. I found cases described which seemed to correspond exactly to my condition, and, most thrilling of all, something could be done about it! Heavens! To be natural, normal and free again! No more sickening spasms of inferiority among other people! To be just like any of these un-self-conscious folk around me whom I had envied for so long! . . . Words failed me.

Words did fail me so utterly that I composed several letters to Mr. Sava before I summoned courage to post one of them. Then there were four awful days waiting for a reply. Was he in London? Would he be able to see me? And—ghastly thought!—would he be able to do anything in my case, after all?

At last the reply came . . . Yes, he could see me next week.

I lived in a whirl and ferment for that week, each day and hour seeming more prolonged than ever; but eventually the day came, and with nervous apprehension, I went for my appointment.

I admit that I was frightened—not of Mr. Sava, nor of thoughts of an operation, but terrified lest all my hopes should be dashed, that an operation might be impossible in my case, or that nothing could be done till after the war. I purposely allowed myself very little time to reach Harley Street so that I should have to run and not have the leisure to think too much—so finally I arrived rather breathless.

What a relief that interview was! The quiet of the consulting-room after the bustle of London outside; Mr. Sava's quick understanding and kindliness for all the psychological inferiority I felt; and, at last, the allaying of all my fears by the assurance that an operation was possible and could be performed as soon as I wished. I reached at that moment a pinnacle of happiness that was a milestone in my life; it was like shaking off a heavy cloak with the knowledge that I need never again struggle along under its weight.

At the same time, I felt curiously stunned, and it was only Mr. Sava's voice that brought me back to earth. He was telling me to think about it and let him know . . . Think about it! When I could have the operation as soon as I chose! Why not tomorrow? I asked. It was gently suggested to me that it should be in a week's time . . . after all there were some other patients besides me. And then I laughed happily as gratitude and joy overcame me. We agreed on the time. Nothing could have been better arranged for me, as I knew that, if necessary, I could take my holiday at that time to allow a sufficient period for the operation and subsequent recovery.

Once again, however, I lived in an agony of mind for a whole week. Suppose anything should happen to Mr. Sava . . . suppose war conditions should make the whole thing impossible after all . . . surely the Fates could not be so unkind . . . They were not; and at the end of that week, which had seemed a veritable eternity, I found myself on the way to the nursing home, ready for the operation the next day. I spent the evening resting—the last thing of which I felt capable, for no book could hold my attention, and writing or any other occupation seemed futile. But somehow the night passed, and I was grateful for the sleeping tablets.

So the great day dawned. I lay in bed restlessly keeping my eye on my watch. I was torn between regret that I should not be able to watch the operation and relief that I should not know anything about it. I speculated on what I should feel like when I woke—a new and free person! Actually, I supposed gloomily, I should feel sick . . .

After another period of seemingly interminable waiting, I was given a sedative, and then, feeling distinctly unsteady,

I went into the operating theatre on the arm of a sympathetic nurse.

There was an air of busy, efficient movement in the room, and the whole atmosphere seemed charged with pleasant anticipation—but I smiled a little grimly to reflect that I was the focus of all this activity. I lay on the operating table, determined not to feel as though I had entered a torture-chamber. I assumed what I no doubt fondly imagined was a naturally pleasant expression in the hope that no-one would realize that at the last moment I could scarcely restrain my-self from bounding out of the theatre and putting as great a distance as possible between myself and the surgeon's knife. I thought I was bluffing very well, and began to congratu-late myself. And then, to my intense annoyance, the anaes-thetist, in all kindness, told me not to look so frightened. I felt a wave of resentment and irritation that he had seen through my acting, and I snapped out some ungracious reply. It did not soothe my ruffled temper when he smiled know-ingly and patted my arm. Days later, I wished I could have apologized, though he obviously realized my feelings and understood.

As in all times of great nervous excitement, everything around me impressed itself with extraordinary vividness upon my memory. Even now I can see clearly in my mind's eye, that curious freckle on the nurse's arm, the stripes of Mr. Sava's shirt, and a host of other quite trivial details. Then the anaesthetist approached with a little syringe which he put in my arm, at the same time telling me to count. Obediently I did as I was told, wondering what was going to happen. I remember Mr. Sava, with his back towards me, washing at the sink and making some light-hearted joke to the nurse, and I was just about to interject a mut-tered "heartless wretch" between "fourteen" and "fifteen" when . . . I knew no more.

The next I knew was waking in my room, asking if it was all over, and then shutting my eyes hurriedly in case it was not. That night passed as a confusion of waking and dozing, of dreams and nurses, of knocking over some water.

Later I awoke to find the night-sister offering me that typically English panacea, a cup of tea, with the remark that it would keep me alive till breakfast time. After she had gone I contemplated the cup as something strange, vaguely wondering at the same time if I was really interested in being kept alive or not. What was the matter with me, I thought. Having gone so far and being now presumably on the road to recovery and freedom, there must be none of this sinking into the slough of despond. With firm resolve I started to sit up suddenly in bed—and equally suddenly sat back. Yes, the horizontal position was definitely preferable. I made a mental note to try it inch by inch next time . . . Oh, blow, sugar in the tea!

The rest of that morning was a hazy dream. Waking life did not seem particularly attractive, so I escaped into unconsciousness. Then lunch. Lunch! Why on earth couldn't they let me sleep in peace? Oh, well, let's see what there is . . . Ugh—Hot milk! Ugh! again. Prunes. I darkly suspected they had found out my pet aversions on purpose. Dreamland was decidedly better than these interruptions.

Tea again. But this time they had remembered I didn't like sugar, thank goodness. And the scone tasted quite good —I certainly must be improving. But the only thing I really wanted was, of course, almost unobtainable—fruit.

From that hour on, I felt better and better. After the first two days of soreness, slight nausea, and chilly depression, I confess I thoroughly enjoyed being spoilt. The daily routine passed comfortably, and all my wants were supplied. In due course, the stitches were removed. Within a week I was allowed to get up and dress—at the end of which exhausting process I was glad to sink into a chair by the fire. A few days later, however, I began to think that that was child's play, and I was delighted to be taken for a short walk in the garden. But I was surprised and alarmed to find out how much concentration that venture seemed to demand. At the end of a fortnight, I felt just a little weak, admittedly; but apart from that I felt perfectly capable of coping with normal life once more, and I left the nursing home, quite regretfully saying goodbye to the nurses. I had still to take a few days' holiday before resuming my work.

Resuming work! How utterly different everything seemed now in these familiar surroundings! It was as though I had been looking at life and Nature through darkened glasses, but now could see clearly and in full perspective and colour. The radiant sunshine echoed the vitality that was in me. All that I hoped for from this operation had been fulfilled.

Now, I am free and happy in a way I never dreamed I ever should be. Naturally, psychologically, physiologically, and in appearance, I felt on an equality with those around me. Never again need I endure that shrinking fear due to the consciousness of abnormality and the sensitiveness that goes with it. It is impossible for me to find words adequate to describe the change in my life. It is strange how often words are a wholly ineffective instrument of expression.

The emotional conflicts of another person often appear exaggerated to the outsider, because, I suppose, one cannot impart acute intensity of feeling to another person. For that reason, I will not enter into any detailed description of my own life, but I feel I must mention one extraordinarily marked effect of the anaesthetic during the operation, because of its great interest to me. If it were not for the undoubtedly pleasant, though temporary, after effects I should certainly recommend a short state of anaesthesia to anyone worried or in a quandary. Before the operation, I had been exceedingly perplexed about a number of problems, including one that involved what would probably be the most important decision of my life; and it is of this I would speak.

For some time, a very close and intimate friend had been asking me to marry him, but although I believed that I was indeed in love, I hung back because of the vague doubts that occasionally stirred within me. Growing up is a difficult business. When one is young, it is so torturingly difficult to try to see the wood apart from the trees, and at times almost impossible. One can but marry a human being and if self-analysis is carried too far at such a stage, one becomes inextricably involved in a tangle of doubts and anxieties, largely because one cannot escape oneself for a single moment. So it was with me.

Yet while I was under the anaesthetic, it was as though my spirit became detached from my earthly body and soared above the world to view things from afar, so that I could see not only this problem in particular, but also many others, both personal and general. More than that, I could see them in their proper perspective.

The result was startling. When I recovered my faculties fully, I felt a different being, able to see my way clearly. So many things were seen in their true light, and now I knew, without the slightest hesitation, that marriage was not my course. Difficult though I knew it was going to be to say the thing and act upon it, it was sheer joy to be relieved from the agony of indecision.

Perhaps only those who have experienced it can understand the curiously empty, lonely feeling that such a decision can bring. The very act of loving and being loved in return fills one with a glow that transcends all other feelings, a serenity and wellbeing of mind and body that nothing else in life can bring so spontaneously. If this glorious interchange is broken, even of one's own volition, the mental pain is intense. It is incommunicable to others in its entirety. But even in this I was strengthened and comforted in great measure by the loyalty and sympathy of my friends. I shall never forget one day, not long after the operation, a friend came to see me and kissed me quite simply in tenderness and affection. It quite dispelled my self-pitying loneliness; and that, combined with the beautiful results of the operation, has completely restored my self-confidence and self-respect.

Three months later, I spent a long week-end in Wales. It was an energetic holiday, including climbing up Snowdon, a walk up Carnedd-Llewelyn, and long cycle rides over the passes among the hills. It was a convincing testimony indeed to the success of the operation and my complete recovery. While I was there, I soared to one of those rare and exhilarating heights of the spirit possible, I think, only in solitude and in the midst of Nature. A man's moments of true serenity are few, but those few will sustain him for a lifetime. It only required one of those moments of serenity on a mountain-top to crystallize and make a stable part of me all the adjustments and new depths of understanding that centred round my operation. My gratitude for the changes wrought then, both physical and psychological, will never cease.

. . . I finished reading this account and thought that now I knew, for the first time, what it was like on the other side of the counter. It was the account of an experience vividly lived through by a woman of unusual sensibility. Yet what did I know, after all? What new thing had I learnt?

I turned the pages again, studying them more closely. There was little here of reactions to the simple surgery of the affair. I knew all about those moments of fear in the theatre, that queer world in which waking seems like dreaming and dreams simulate reality, which is the essence of post-anaesthesia. I had here something more valuable, something more profound than any account of physical events could be.

For what these simple words told with such sincerity was the reawakening of a mind and a spirit, a restoration not so much of the comeliness of a human body as of the poise of a mind upon which shadows had too long rested. It seemed as though the surgeon's knife had cut deeper than even I believed it could and that what one cuts away is not simply muscle and tissue but the intangible accretions of the human soul.

And even at that, I am still far from the truth. Covering that absorbing story of the voyage of a mind from storm to serenity was a friendly and charming note. She apologizes for the inadequacy of her story: ". . . I feel impotent and rather frustrated, myself," she says. "I find it impossible to put a great deal of the personal side in, and therefore I feel I have failed miserably in what I wanted to write. There are many personal things of mind and spirit which are a vital and essential part of an individual's life and character, which are yet incapable of expression in words before a general public . . ."

For all its depth, then, there are still deeps unsounded. For all its revelation, there is much still hidden. The thought makes me humble. For how can I, or anyone, know what springs are unlocked by the tasks of the daily round?

Perhaps one should not pry into the secrets of the other side of the counter. Perhaps one should be satisfied to do one's job and be grateful when it is well done. And yet it is glimpses like this that are among the most stimulating of all experiences, raising the work of the surgeon above a mere matter of art and science and technique and integrating it with the very stuff of life itself.

VIII

A BOLD DECISION

I had known Margery for a long time. Many times we had partnered each other at the tennis club of which we were both members, and it was there she met her future husband, who also at times had been a partner of mine. Often in those dimly recalled years of before the war—they seem to belong to a different age!—I thought how happily and ideally matched they were. It was not simply that they were both physically attractive and good-natured. They seemed, at any rate to an outsider, to share so many interests in common.

It was just before the outbreak of war in 1939 that they were married. I sent them my congratulations, which in this instance at least were not merely formal, and I hoped to spend happy hours with them again. But then the war came, sweeping away much of one's normal routine. I quite lost sight of them, though occasionally news of them reached me. Every hope seemed to be justified from the information I had from those who knew them. They were the perfectly married couple. But what a pity it was, so many remarked, they did not have any children . . .

From the outbreak of war to my seeing Margery again was almost exactly three years. Apart from the trickle of gossip that reached me I knew practically nothing about her nowadays, but I had nevertheless been delighted to see her name entered in my book for an appointment later in the day. She had made the hour so late that I concluded it was a personal and not a professional visit.

"It's nice to see you again," I said, as she was shown into my room. "I forget how long it is since we last met, but in any case it's far too long. I hope you come as a friend for a chat and not as a patient for a consultation." But as I spoke the words I felt no confidence. She looked worried and distraught. "How's John?" I added.

"Oh, he's fine," she replied, and she told me what he was doing now. "But I've come to see you, George, partly as a friend and partly as a doctor. I mean, I want to consult you because I believe that, as a friend as well, you will tell me the truth. That sounds horribly complicated and ominous, doesn't it? But I think you get what I mean."

"I think so. You look worried. What's the trouble?" I returned. And I wondered whether it was some problem of her married life she had come to discuss.

"Well . . ." She hesitated and appeared suddenly bashful, an unusual state for her. She was not a bold girl, but she was always frank and open, and this reluctance to speak helped to confirm my belief that it was rather a domestic problem than a medical one she had come to discuss. "It's like this, George," she went on slowly. "No two people could be happier together than John and I are. It's wonderful," she said, and the glow in her eyes was even more eloquent than her words, "but—well, there's one thing that rather casts a shadow over it. You see, both of us are desperately keen to have children, and though we've tried and tried—well, as you know, nothing happens."

"So you're not the modern type who tends to despise children," I returned. "And what do you expect me to do about it?"

I was talking to her more as a friend than as a doctor. It was the better way.

"I don't know. You see, as soon as we realized our efforts were all in vain, we naturally suspected that one or other of us must have something wrong, so I went to the doctor. He's a nice old boy, though he's getting a bit doddery, and but for the war, he says, he would have retired."

"Well?"

"What he told me," she continued seriously, with her head bent, "shocked us both terribly. He said it would be impossible for me ever to have a child."

"Eh?" I sat up sharply. "Did he tell you why?"

She nodded. "Yes. He said I wasn't properly developed or something."

I frowned. This was a very rash statement on the face of it. Margery was, to all outward appearances, a thoroughly normal young woman; and it is part of every normal woman's make-up to be able to have a child. I thought of the mental picture her description of the doctor had conjured up: old, doddery, and wanting to retire. Probably he knew little or nothing about the subject at all.

"But that's an absurd thing to say. Did he examine you?"

"Not much. He asked me a lot of questions, and then he said, 'I'm afraid there's only one conclusion to arrive at—you'll never be able to have a child if you haven't had one by now.' And so that was that."

"So you've come to see me to find out if I can say anything different?"

"Yes. John thought it would be a good idea, because you wouldn't be just a stranger, and as a friend you'd tell me the truth. If it really is like that, then we shall have to face it and give up the idea, though that would be as big a blow to John as it would be to me. But if there's some hope . . . Well, both of us are ready to face any reasonable risk."

"I can't say yes or no, as things are. I know nothing about you medically. You'd better come along next week and I'll give you a thorough examination. But you can take it from me that people aren't sterile for no reason at all. There's some definite cause for it, and if we can find that cause we may be able to do something about it."

"Oh, thank you, George," she exclaimed. "Even that gives me a little more hope. It seemed so awful. After all, I've been fit and clean all my life."

"Exactly," I replied. "That's the very reason you shouldn't despair."

A little later she left me. The position was the more ridiculous the more I thought about it. This doctor had asked her a few questions as the result of which he had arrived at a sweeping, dogmatic statement that could be justified only by the most searching investigation. More than that, it took for granted that, if sterility existed, it lay in Margery herself and quite ignored the fact that, in modern civilization, sterility is at least as common in men as in women; indeed, there is something more than a suggestion that it is more prevalent among men. I felt annoyed at this dictum, not merely because it was casual and unscientific, but because it had been given in such a way as to cause acute mental distress to the patient. Its finality, too, was another thing against it. The majority of people would probably have accepted it as the last word to be said and not taken even the precaution of another and perhaps more expert opinion.

My doubts were increased at the first examination. So far as the most rigorous external examination could reveal, Margery was a perfectly healthy, normal woman. Her desire for motherhood was extremely strong. There was nothing at all on which to base even a tentative opinion that here was a sterile woman. What then, was wrong?

The only way to find out was, I decided, to make an exploratory operation. I told her, and she did not shrink from the idea. On the contrary she welcomed it. She felt, I think, that this at least would decide the matter. It was taking the case to the last court of appeal, and if the verdict was adverse then it would have to be accepted for what it was. But at least there would be no torturing doubts left.

As I expected, she asked me if I would undertake the operation and I readily agreed. I was determined to do my best for her. She had suffered enough already, first from the thwarting of her hopes, and then from the rebuff she had received when, like a prudent person, she had sought advice.

In due course she was admitted to a nursing home, and I performed the operation. In thinking over the case, several possibilities had occurred to me, as they must, but even so, though I had passed everything in review, I was not fully prepared for what I did in fact find. There was a small growth at the apex of the womb, no bigger than a walnut and not in itself of any great danger, but sufficient to inhibit pregnancy. Everything else was normal. If that doctor had been able to diagnose this condition from his cursory examination, he was a genius; but I still doubted it. And in any case the condition was not beyond remedy.

I excised this growth and Margery's subsequent recovery was perfectly normal. Her case never gave me the slightest anxiety; in fact, she revealed a degree of physical stamina beyond even what might have been expected from a woman of her age and fitness.

When two months later, the news reached me that she was pregnant, I felt that final glow of satisfaction that comes when one of one's ambitions is realized. Once more she came to me for advice, as I had told her that though I could now see no bar to the gratification of her wishes and her husband's, any pregnancy would have to be treated with some care. John had given her full permission to seek the finest treatment possible, and now here she was asking me what she should do.

After some thought I decided that the best course was to send her to one of the leading hospitals, where they had a gynaecologist of considerable reputation. To this specialist I wrote a letter, and it was here I made a bad tactical blunder that was to have tragic consequences. I gave in great detail an account of the case,—and then I was rash enough not merely to express an opinion, but to do so in the most emphatic terms. I said that, taking everything into consideration, this patient must have a Caesarean operation.

Now there is no pride more easily touched than that of an expert, whether he be doctor or stamp-collector, scientist or art critic. The slightest suggestion that anyone in another field should have views about his own raises at once what psychologists call a violent defence reaction. So it happened now. This gynaecologist no doubt resented the unwarranted intrusion of a mere general surgeon into his own special province. What did such a jack-of-all-trades know of

Caesarean operations and the conditions under which they were imperative?

He examined Margery and gave his decision. He informed her, with the weight of his vast authority and his impressive personality, that he saw no reason why she should not undergo a normal delivery.

When Margery told me this, I confess I was a little dismayed, but it was not for me to challenge such authority, and I had no wish to invite further trouble by embarking on a conflict of opinions. I advised Margery to take the recommended course. The gynaecologist was now in charge of her, and it would be unfair to him to question his opinions.

She seemed quite content. Her main thought was that she was going to have a baby, and if it could be normal in every possible way, so much the better. It would wipe away the last trace of those nightmare months when she had considered her ambitions quite unattainable.

There, it seemed, my connexion with the case ended. I had done all that had been asked of me and received a quite disproportionate measure of gratitude in return. And, even though at times when I thought of it, a vague doubt of the gynaecologist's wisdom crossed my mind, I was on the whole content to leave it at that. I was not at all ready for what followed.

It was some months later when I was told that John wished to see me very urgently. He had left no message what the trouble was, but merely said he was coming at once and hoped I would be able to see him.

It was an utterly distracted man who walked—perhaps staggered is the better word—into my room. He bore little resemblance to the active, confident young man whose forehand drive and volleys on the tennis court were the despair of all his opponents and a constant problem to the club secretary who had to replace the balls they wore out so quickly. His hair was dishevelled. He looked as though he had had little sleep and that in his clothes. Most startling of all, tears stood in his eyes as he looked at me.

"George," he said hoarsely. "I need you. Margery needs you."

"What's the matter?" I exclaimed. His distress was so real that one could not doubt the urgency of his call.

And then he told me, in broken, harsh sentences, that somehow were like knives cutting into one's brain. They had taken Margery to a country hospital, and there they waited for normal labour to develop. Three days passed, but nothing happened. The danger signals were hoisted in an unmistakable way. First her blood pressure began to rise ominously until at last it reached a dangerously alarming height. Her kidneys, those barometers of the body, started to show signs of tiredness.

But still the aid of the surgeon was not invoked. The Caesarean section, for which this case cried out, was not performed. Instead, labour was induced by instrumental means. For twelve hours, that girl was torn on a rack of agony. And in the end, the child was delivered—a girl.

The odds were too heavy against the child. The mother's high blood pressure and its own long-drawn-out suffering doomed it. Haemorrhage of the brain set in, and within eight hours the baby was dead.

I stood aghast. It was a case of which no-one could be anything but ashamed. And it was the more damnable in that I believed all this agony could have been avoided but for my own mismanagement of a few words and for the wounded pride of a specialist who thought his own reputation more important than the inference to be drawn from the facts before him.

"There's nothing I can do now," I said quietly. "But if I can help you, I will."

"See her," he said appealingly. "She trusts in you. Of course, she's still in hospital. But after that, how can I have any faith in them at all?"

I went to see her. She was in a terribly weak condition, and I fully shared the doubts of her survival confidentially imparted to me. All depended on her own sound constitution. I knew she was extremely fit, and therein lay her one hope.

For three months that battle for life lasted. But at last she won through, though the marks of the struggle still showed in her face and in the loss of elasticity in her movements. And when she was discharged from hospital, she was told, with great gravity, that her heart and kidneys were now so weak that she must not on any account risk another pregnancy, the outcome of which would certainly be fatal to her.

So perhaps in view of all that happened, I may be excused if, when I heard she and John had made an appointment with me, I felt a little apprehensive. Though the fault did not lie entirely or even to the greater extent with me, I felt a grave responsibility. I half expected reproaches for raising hopes that had been so disastrously denied. It was, I know, disloyal of me to think these things, but I could not escape that feeling of guilt.

I have rarely seen a woman more depressed. Of course, in part that was due to all she had experienced. Things like that leave their mark on the mind no less than on the body; and when the body is cured the mental wounds remain, for they heal more slowly and less certainly, sometimes leaving an ugly scar. But that was not the principal cause. Not even all her agony had lessened her desire that she should have a child. The wish had become almost an obsession. She was convinced that now, even more than before, all her happiness lay in that; unless she became a mother, life would lose all point and interest for her.

Once again, then, she asked me the question she had asked before. Was it utterly impossible for her to have a child?

I went over the whole details of the case. I considered it from every angle. The risks involved were so great that no-one could ignore them. And yet, what were the risks if she did not have a child? Her life would become a perpetual torture. She would know neither peace nor repose. Eventually, it might be, she would grow embittered and deny even her love for her husband. They were psychological risks against physical ones, almost incompatible and therefore not to be weighed one against the other; yet it had to be done.

I took all my courage in my hands. I made a bold—some would say a foolhardy—decision. I looked at her gravely.

"There are risks," I said slowly. "Very great risks. But it is not utterly impossible for you to have a child, and with careful attention you might get through. Against that, I consider that your life will be ruined if you leave things as you are. If you want a perfectly frank opinion, I say not merely that you *can* have a child, but that you *must*."

Once again I had used that fatal word "must". It was, as I thought then, an unhappy omen.

"Thank you, George," she said quietly. "You are so very understanding. The risks don't matter. I fear life as it is far more."

But I warned her she must take care. It would not do to act on this advice too soon. She must be quite sure that she felt strong enough in herself.

Good advice, no doubt. But the urge to realize her hopes was too strong, and it was only two or three months later that I heard with some alarm that she was pregnant again. This was very much sooner than I could have wished.

She looked much happier when she came to see me. John was with her and there was a charming air of solicitude in his attitude towards her—though it was a solicitude not untinged with a secret fear. Great as his desire to have a child was, it was less than the dread of losing his beloved wife.

"George," he said, "you have been a good friend to us. We want to ask another favour of you. Will you undertake this case right through?"

I did not altogether welcome the idea at first.

"It's a case for a gynaecologist—an obstetrician," I replied. "That's not my speciality."

John made a gesture of contempt and annoyance. "I have had enough of specialists of that kind," he snapped. "No, George, you are the only doctor in whom Margery and I have any trust now."

I pondered. It was quite true that this was really quite outside my practice, yet there were other factors. I still had that feeling of guilt to expunge, and after the previous experience I shared to some extent John's doubt of others. It was a special case. In a unique way, it was my own. More than that, this pregnancy was the direct outcome of advice I had given in direct opposition to that given by the hospital where Margery had been so long under treatment. That alone was something I could not shirk. Having given it, in the full knowledge of what I was doing, I could hardly at this stage, when it had been acted upon, try to shift the burden to someone else. Moreover, taking all the circumstances into account, it might be that no other doctor would accept the case.

"Very well," I said, though making no effort to hide my reluctance, "I will do so, if you wish."

"Thank you, George," said Margery. "You've lifted a load from our minds."

The regimen I laid down for her was extremely strict. She was placed at a very early stage in a nursing home, in the staff of which I had complete faith; and there she was tended in an absolutely exemplary manner. We watched her with the utmost care—almost with the closeness of a research worker keeping his living specimens under observation. The risks were big. Our only hope was to meet them, if they occurred, at the very first and faintest sign.

And for eight months, it seemed as though all these elaborate precautions were, if not unnecessary, at any rate an excess of caution. But at the beginning of the ninth month, the red light flashed. And it was the very one I had most dreaded, the one, among all the possibilities, I wished least to see.

Once again her blood pressure chart began to rise steeply. I admit that from that moment my nights were sleepless. Every ring on the telephone gave me a start of fear, for I imagined it might be the urgent summons to her bedside. But somehow or other it was kept just under control.

Two weeks before the full term of pregnancy, I performed a Caesarean section. Every moment was tense, but at last it was done. We had succeeded—so far. History seemed to be repeating itself, for the baby was a girl. I had the curious feeling that I had turned back the clock and been given another chance of doing what I should have done in the first place—an opportunity not often given to a man. And perhaps, I thought, the chance is undeserved.

When I left the nursing home, I was still filled with doubts. There were anxious moments still to pass. The telephone bell could still be, as it so often is for a doctor, the tocsin of fate. But that night it did not ring. The last report I had was that everything was satisfactory.

I set out early for the home the next morning, and I was somewhat alarmed when the matron asked me to go at once to Margery's room. Had some sudden crisis developed after all, then?

"I think you should see her now," said the matron seriously.

I braced myself for a shock. Shock, indeed, I experienced, but it was not at all what I expected. Not merely was Margery in fine fettle; she was actually sitting up in bed and eating her breakfast. On a chair, gazing at her with adoring eyes, was John. His glance passed to me dumbly, as though joy and relief had robbed him of all powers of speech. And then, slowly, like a man in a dream he rose and held out his hand.

The simple, sincere gesture was more eloquent even than the torrent of phrases of gratitude it released.

"We can never thank you enough, George," said Margery; and John nodded silently.

"Rubbish!" I replied. "I have to thank you both for trusting in my decision. You've behaved admirably, Margery. You're the real heroine of this story. It needed courage to run the risk you did. It's all turned out well, but it could just as easily have been tragedy. Perhaps even more easily," I added.

They shook their heads in unison. It was difficult to get away.

Yes, it might so easily have been tragedy—a deeper tragedy even than the first had been. For it had been a bold decision I had made. If I had been wise and spoken according to the book of caution, I should never have made it. Nothing is more reprehensible in a doctor than to make decisions lightly in matters of life and death. Yet it is just there that the questions begin to arise.

There are things not mentioned in the bulky tomes that line my reference bookshelves. They can tell me all I may want to know about this or that disease, about how authorities disagree, or alternative procedures. But they never talk of joy and happiness. Surgeons, faced with facts, tend to forget those things. Yet can there be life without them? Is life without them really life? There are people who would take any risk for happiness, yet would not move an inch merely to ensure the continuity of their mere existence. The surgeon, too, must be on the side of the angels sometimes.

And that reminds me that they christened her Angela. I was present at the ceremony, for I had asked to be godfather. This child, in a very special sense, was mine to sponsor. If I looked at it with pride and thankfulness, that was as nothing to the happy glow on the faces of her parents. In bringing one more life into the world, I had made an entity of three.

IX

UNFULFILLED DIVORCE

Medicine can never be the exact science that some people think it should be. If the doctor knew all the facts and laws about the human body, he could never base his decisions entirely upon those alone, as the engineer and the physicist do in their own spheres of work. The doctor's material is a human being, with all the prejudices, ethical and material, that make up the individual human personality. If the observed data point scientifically to one inescapable conclusion that this or the other is the right course of treatment, then it is quite likely that the patient himself will adduce some particular private reason why that treatment is the very one to which he cannot agree. The grounds may be religious; they may be simply emotional. So, too, in medicine one must sometimes take a course that the basic science of the situation hardly justifies, merely because there are psychological factors that make it highly desirable. Medicine is, as has often been remarked, the meeting place of art and science; but it is also something more—an adventure in the ways of human souls, an education in humanity in its widest sense.

My thoughts were turned that way by the memory of the case of Eve. It was a curious case in which scientific necessity and religious scruples became hopelessly entangled in a way that seemed impossible to unravel. And it was also one of those cases in which the surgeon's knife cut away not merely bodily tissue but also the weeds of unhappiness that had grown round two lives.

In her teens, Eve had been one of the beauties of her year, and when she came to see me, then in the late twenties, she was still strikingly handsome, though there was an air of shyness about her that seemed quite out of character. I have come to recognize that particular expression. It arises from a feeling of self-consciousness due to some abnormality. The air of unnaturalness about it is due, I think, not so much to its being something alien grafted onto the person's character, as to its being almost exactly similar to the shyness of adolescence—due also to self-consciousness—and thus being quite out of place in a man or woman of mature years. The suggestion of *gaucherie* about it has none of the natural simplicity of the normally shy and retiring individual.

Eve had married some years before, and the match had proved successful in every way. She and her husband were seen everywhere together, obviously happy in each other's presence. A couple of years after the marriage, Eve had her first child, and, though her doctor was dubious about the wisdom of the course, she insisted on feeding it herself. The results were now plain to see. I had recognized them at once as the fountain of her shyness. It was a type of abnormality that always induces acute self-consciousness in women, as I have told elsewhere: hypertrophy of the breasts. The immediate cause, I learnt on looking into her case, was a disturbance in the secretions of the endocrine glands, the outcome of her feeding her child.

Now her attitude towards me, a stranger, was embarrassing enough in its air of withdrawal and fear that I might be criticizing her. But as led on by sympathetic handling she unfolded the whole of her story, I realized that it was a very serious menace to her whole life. This abnormality was producing a state that was starkly psychopathological, for it resulted in a degree of bashfulness that was coming between her and her husband—who, incidentally, as I was later to find out for myself, was an extremely understanding and tactful man, of whom no-one, least of all his wife, need have stood in fear.

By the time she came to consult me, she had already reached the stage when she could not bear to allow her husband to see her undressed, while the mere suggestion of the intimate relations of marriage produced a feeling almost of nausea in her. And these were the starting points of possible tragedy.

At first, her husband treated her with consideration, but as she withdrew further and further from him, he began to wonder if there was not something else behind it than mere embarrassment. Doubts of her continued love for him rose in his mind; and the more she insisted that it was merely her appearance that worried her, the more he felt that this was a mere excuse and that he must look further afield if he was to find the real cause.

Suspicion is a plant that flourishes quickly once the seeds have been planted, and in this case it did not belie its reputation. Vague uneasiness deepened into unhappiness, and unhappiness into open discord. The mutual understanding that had marked the early days of their marriage disappeared, and its place was taken by mistrust. Each laid the blame on the other. An accusation denied was taken as proof of guilt. The story is too familiar to students of humanity to need repeating in great detail. It ran its appointed course until it reached that point at which a decision must be taken—a decision that must set the scene for the whole of their lives. And here there seemed only one logical outcome: divorce.

It is a curious thing that two people may quarrel every time they meet and their day to day lives together become impossible, but unconsciously the small hope of reconciliation never seems quite to die, and the decision to end it all is rarely taken without reservation and reluctance. Those who argue that all divorce should be by agreement are probably the strongest advocates of harder divorce and not easier divorce, as they suppose themselves to be. It was thus with these two. They agreed upon the desirability of divorce, but for the moment they decided only to separate and live their own lives. They made no legal deed of separation. For the moment, their future hung in the air, since neither had the courage to take the final irrevocable step.

The girl Eve, was supremely unhappy from that moment. In the hope of forgetting her sorrows in arduous work, she took a war job, but it made little difference to her. In her heart, she knew that she still loved her husband, and she believed that all this would never have happened if she had not become the victim of this glandular disorder which had so transformed both her form and her mind.

How often it happens that the map of the way out is produced only when the travellers have gone too far! It was an ironic tragedy indeed that not until the final separation had taken place and the affair seemed ended did a friend of Eve's come to her rescue. This was the one person to whom she confided all the terrible details of her acute inferiority feeling. That friend opened her eyes wide with astonishment. She had always imagined Eve to be a sophisticated girl to whom most things were known; and it came as a shock to her to realize that Eve knew nothing at all about the possibility of a plastic reconstruction.

A new light of hope dawned upon the tortured girl. Bright thoughts of restoring all that had been lost filled her mind, but now fresh difficulties arose. Eve was a Roman Catholic. She feared to run counter to the authority of the Church. In her new dilemma she consulted her father-confessor and laid the whole position before him. He was an old-fashioned man with rigid ideas, and frowned at once on her suggestion. If she had her breasts reconstructed, he pointed out, it might lead to loss of function and she might be unable to feed any further children she might have. The operation was not necessary for her health, so far as anyone knew—at any rate for her physical health, and the Church claims to be able, on its own, to deal with all matters of mental health—and the whole proposal, therefore, was against the tenets of the Faith.

She went away distracted. For a moment a new light had shone in her, the blessed light of hope. Now even that had been killed. And as if to crush her still further at the moment of her deepest sorrow, fresh burdens were piled upon her. Her husband began to insist upon a divorce and was consulting his solicitors. But this, again, was against the laws of the faith of which Eve was a member. Even if her husband secured the divorce he wished for by decree of the English Courts, it would not set her free in the eyes of her own Church. Even if she fell in love again, there could be no fresh start in life for her.

Even then, when it appeared that she was on the point of losing her husband forever, she knew that she still loved him. It was impossible that they could part, ridiculous that the only communication she had with him was through the dry, precise letters sent by his solicitors, who were now, after long discussion, drawing up a deed of separation, her husband having reluctantly admitted the force of her religious scruples.

There seemed no way out of this growing tangle. Each fresh move increased the tragedy. For her, there was nothing at all to which to look forward. She could not be divorced and hope for the chance of starting anew, even if she had wished. She was tied to a hopeless love from which there was no release. Slowly she sank deeper and deeper into despair, from which not even the care of her child could rouse her.

Things were now looking desperate. Her friend was with her constantly, noticing that every day seemed to bring a change for the worse. For, quite apart from the outside troubles, that terrible inferiority feeling was gnawing at her the whole time, each fresh rebuff in the battle of life adding to its strength. It was a slow poison eating away at her very spirit, and her friend now grew seriously alarmed.

She made a great fight to overcome Eve's scruples. There was no harm in seeing me, she pointed out. If nothing could be done, then the matter was settled, once for all. But if it was possible, she ought to see that she owed it to herself and to her child to bring herself back to sanity. So, reluctantly, frightened, and a little antagonistic, she found her way to my consulting-room.

The examination was encouraging. It was by no means an out-of-the way operation that would be involved. The whole thing could be done, and I had no doubts of the outcome.

She nodded, almost without interest. I think she would rather have heard me pronounce her case inoperable.

"Thank you, doctor," she said slowly. "But, of course, I can't have it done."

"Why?" I asked.

She explained the decision of her priest. I shook my head.

"Forgive me," I said, "but surgery is one thing and theology another. I am a Roman Catholic myself, and I would bow to the decision of a priest in any matter of dogma. But when it comes to my own particular province I feel that probably I know a little bit more than a father. You see, his argument is based on a fallacy. There would be absolutely no interference with the normal function of the breasts. Plastic surgery is comparatively new, you know, and a lot of misconceptions exist about it."

Again she shook her head sadly.

"That may be true. I don't dispute it or put Father Colne's opinion above yours, doctor. But I cannot run against his expressed wishes."

I made a mental note of the name. "Very well. But I think you ought to consider it. I can give you details of cases exactly similar to yours in which the patient has subsequently fed her babies."

"I don't think even that would alter his decision," she said. None the less she promised to think it over, though I imagine her words were only a cloak for her inability to give an outright "no" to something that she really desired.

When she had gone, I saw another patient, who was followed by another, for it was a busy day; and it was not until the evening, after dinner, that I was able to give a thought to the case again. An idea struck me, and after some consideration I decided to act upon it. It was the one way out.

It was unorthodox enough. I, a mere surgeon, was going to dispute a ruling of the Church through its priest, Father Colne, It might not serve any useful purpose at all, but it was the only hope. The more I considered Eve's case, the more imperative that operation appeared. Unless it was done, I believed that insanity might easily result.

Next day I called on Father Colne. He greeted me with a very pleasant smile, quite different from what I expected.

The light of humanity twinkled in his eye, and he had an air of good humour. But he was old. And it is difficult to change one's mind when one is old.

I told him bluntly why I had come, but he shook his head, still smiling.

"No, my son," he said, "you are a surgeon and you see these things differently from the Church. I have no doubt you would make a very good job of it if it was undertaken. But it cuts across one of the great principles of the Church. An operation is permissible only to save life or alleviate suffering."

"True," I said, deciding to be bold. "But surely it is vital to ensure mental health as well as physical health? Suffering in the mind is more horrible than most physical pains."

He smiled. "I agree. But we can take care of mental ills."

"Can you—always?" I challenged; and for a moment the smile faded from his face. Perhaps I was being too bold. "You can put ointment on some of the wounds but you cannot always remove the cause. That girl will never be happy while she realizes she is abnormal in appearance and different from everyone else."

He did not reply at once and I lost no time in driving home my attack. I explained what the operation was and how it was done. For an hour I lectured him on anatomy and physiology. I proved to him that there would be no loss of function; on the contrary, Eve would be restored to complete normality.

From time to time, particularly in the early stages, he made small gestures and interjections of dissent, but I would not let him speak. I swamped him with words and dazzled him with examples. At the end I leant back in my chair feeling a trifle exhausted.

He was silent for a little while. Either my onslaught had overpowered him or he was thinking it over. What now? I thought. Will this old gentleman understand? Can he cut away the prejudices and opinions of a lifetime, merely because a surgeon quite unknown to him comes and lectures him in his own study?

Slowly he looked up, and the smile dawned on his face. His grey eyes twinkled happily.

"You argue your case well," he remarked. "I think you have convinced me. You have to realize that I am concerned with something even more precious than human lives—human souls. I have to be certain as I can be that no advice of mine shall imperil their future. It is a grave responsibility, my son—greater even than yours."

"You have altered your opinion?" I asked.

He did not answer directly. "I tell you what I will do. I will see her and talk to her. You say this is necessary for her mental health alone. I can certainly decide on that point out of my own experience. Leave it to me. You shall hear in due course."

There I had to leave it. I had felt hopeful while he had been talking, but as I drove away, doubts surged up in me. He had evaded replying to my direct question. Perhaps I had been too forthright. Perhaps I had said too much. Perhaps . . . But everyone knows this frame of mind. I had fought hard for something I felt was necessary, and now, in relaxation, I was feeling the reaction. There was nothing I could do but wait. But he need not think he had fobbed me off and that he could let the matter drop quietly out of sight. I had gone so far, and so I might go the whole way. If he did not tell me his decision, I would worry him till he did.

But there was no need for this drastic course, which in any event would have been a scurvy return for the courtesy with which I had been treated. The reply came from Eve herself three days later. Could she see me soon? I made an appointment for the next day.

Immediately she came into the room I could see that something had happened. She was still depressed and shy. She was still frightened. But now her eyes were no longer dull. The spark of hope had been kindled in them.

"Thank you, doctor, for seeing Father Colne," she said quietly. "It was good of you to take so much trouble about me."

"It was very unorthodox of me," I replied. "I ran the risk of deeply offending both you and him."

"It makes it all the more charming of you that you took that risk," she continued. "I saw him yesterday and—well, he has admitted that he was wrong. He sees no objection to having the operation done." She looked up with an eagerness I had never yet seen in her. "How soon can I have it done?" she asked.

I made the arrangements. Beds were scarce at that time in the nursing homes, but finally the operation was fixed for two weeks later.

Of the operation I need say little. No difficulties of an unusual kind cropped up, and everything ran smoothly. Nor were there any complications in the critical post-operative stage. Her recovery was neither too fast nor too slow, and she left the home physically and mentally a new woman.

Just another successful operation? That was all I thought then. It had had its interesting features, but they had nothing to do with the surgery of the case, which had been straightforward. It was the first time I had come out in open conflict with the Church—and won the day.

Yes, it was worth while—and not simply for the fact that I had been instrumental in giving back normality and balance of mind to a suffering woman. The operation was but the beginning. It is always the end that matters most.

Eve had not, I knew, had that operation simply to improve her appearance. Love for her husband was still in her, and she yet hoped, I believe, that now she was herself again she stood a chance of returning to him. Unless that happened, she might yet curse me for not leaving her to the misery to which she had grown accustomed. Success would not have been won.

It was at a party she met him again. It was quite casual and unexpected; and he came across to talk to her. At first they might have been strangers meeting for the first time, but gradually their tone became more friendly. He asked her to dine with him the next night. And then they met with increasing frequency. It was courtship all over again, and all the old charm and mutual attraction gradually returned, enriched and deepened by their experiences.

They are together again now. They see that it was all a mistake—one of those mistakes that come of frayed nerves and unbalanced tempers. They look back upon those days as a nightmare that is better forgotten. Perhaps they are happier now than ever for they realize how strongly they are bound together. They have cemented the remade bond with another child—a boy.

Just after his birth, the husband rang me up. Would I do them a favour? he asked with the shy eagerness of a small boy asking for a second helping of his favourite sweet. What was it? I asked. Might they give the child the middle name of "Sava"?—it was an unusual name for an English boy, but then the whole circumstances were unusual . . . Oh, and by the way, Eve is feeding him herself, and Father Colne thinks he is a delightful baby . . .

X

TUBERCULOSIS IS NOT INCURABLE

Ambition is a strange thing. It will drive a man on relentlessly, forcing him to overcome obstacles that to a more balanced view might well seem insurmountable. It will compel him to use up energy at a rate that the human system can hardly supply. And in the end, high ambition, with its ceaseless drive, often defeats its own ends. For in bringing a man to the thing it seeks it denies him full enjoyment, since all his physical resources have been spent in the attainment.

The man who has become rich from poverty-stricken beginnings and finds himself blessed with everything that money can buy but happiness, is the dominant example of the case of ambition which defeats itself. But even more tragic is the case of the man who ruins his health because the spur has been dug in too hard. He is the natural sport of the Fates, who placing the prize in his hands paralyse his grasp so that he cannot hold it.

Every day these untold tragedies occur. They hit no headlines because often they are concerned with the little things that are big in life but trivial in the eyes of news editors. But sometimes it is possible to outwit cruel destiny and turn tragedy into fulfilment almost at the eleventh hour. When one has been instrumental in such a case one feels a rich glow of satisfaction.

It was given to me to take part in such a last-minute rescue not so very long ago. The principal actor was only twenty-eight when I met him, but already it seemed that he had tasted in his short life most of its bitterness as well as its sweets. He struck me from the first as unusually alert and intelligent, though he was suffering deeply when I met him.

He was, in fact, the most pathetic of human tragedies—the man whom serious illness is robbing prematurely of a reward well won.

There had been no privileges in Peter's life. At an early age he had lost his parents and he had had to fend for himself. He had had no particular education, apart from what the State provided, and even when he was at school he had been glad enough to earn an odd shilling by rising early to do a newspaper round. As a child he had known what it was to go hungry.

But he had one great advantage over most other boys in his position. He had a remarkably strong sense of vocation. He knew what, above all else, he wanted to be; and the passing years but added to his determination to attain his goal. The sheer impossibility, on the surface, of achieving it spurred him on.

His ambition was one which, in the rough and tumble of the life he had to lead, he learnt to keep fairly much to himself. One day he believed he would be a famous dress designer. To most of his companions this ambition seemed horribly and guiltily effeminate. If he had been convinced of his destiny to be a soldier, an airman, an engine-driver, even a pastrycook, he would have been understood. But dress designing is something that the English regard as rather beneath a man's dignity. True, a certain section of the English public looks upon the male dress designers of Paris as only a little lower than the angels, but those same people would feel embarrassed and even shamed if a son of theirs openly avowed his intention of studying dress design for himself. Let him be a lawyer, a clergyman, perhaps an engineer or a doctor, and he would bring no disgrace upon the family. But dress designing? Oh, no; it would be too terribly shocking.

And Peter had his own ideas of what sort of a designer he wanted to be. As he grew older, he derived immense delight from seeing girls well dressed. He had, from the first, an unerring eye. Yet he had no ambition to rise to the heights, adopt a French name, and design gowns that would sell in the West End for a hundred or so guineas each and grace the form of some rich woman. His thoughts had a more idealistic trend; he wanted to see all women well dressed as the result of his efforts. He wanted to work for the many and bring them happiness and satisfaction. The rich, he felt, could look after themselves; they always had been able to.

Now it is an amazing thing that Fate always seems to slam doors in the face of a man fired with a real ambition. It is as though his sincerity must be fully tested. There was no opening, it seemed, in the dress trade for Peter. Other boys and young men found no difficulty at all in securing positions as machinists or even messengers in various places, though the work to them was only a means of making a living neither more nor less desirable than others.

Peter had to take what he could—and that was not in the dress trade. He became a waiter. The satisfaction of having a position, however humble, in the trade he wished to serve was denied him. Instead, he was thrown into an occupation which brought him in daily contact with well-dressed women. Perhaps it eased his mind a little to have opportunities of studying what these women wore and how they wore it. But it got him no further towards his goal—on the face of it.

Yet nothing could damp his ardour. He attended an L.C.C. Institute and took classes in dressmaking and designing. He worked at home. He even found the chance to utilize odd moments in the restaurant, somewhat shaking the equanimity of the head waiter and his colleagues by now and then draping his white napkin against the black of his coat as some effect struck him.

There was no time for relaxation in his life. He kept apart from other men of his own age. While they went to football matches or the pictures, Peter worked. Where they spent their spare money on drinks or saved it up for an annual holiday by the sea, Peter laid out every penny he could spare on books, on pieces of material to try out experiments, on drawing materials so that he could practise his sketching. He did not allow himself any time for exercise. He was a man with one ruling passion to which everything else had to be subordinated. A waiter's life can be very tiring and trying; but it always left Peter with sufficient energy to carry on with his studies. The work, in fact, was only the means by which he managed to keep body and soul together, and it was his day off that gave him his real purpose in life.

At the evening classes he met a girl who was extremely charming. She was the one human being who had ever had the power to distract his attention for even a little while from his studies. He found himself growing more and more fascinated by her, looking for her as soon as he entered the classroom, feeling vaguely uneasy if, as happened once or twice, she was not there.

He had not had much experience of other human beings. His attitude towards them was governed largely by those hard-and-fast rules we call convention. He talked to her a little, but never felt at ease. She was something distinct from him, a visitor from another world. In vain he tried to tell himself that he had no time for women, that he must defer thoughts of that kind till he had gone further along the path he had chosen. It was of no avail. He had at last to confess to himself that he loved her—loved her with a passion that was almost as driving as that for his work.

He confessed it to himself—yes; but that was as far as he got. He was, as I say, ruled by conventional ideas, some of which had been intensified by his work as a waiter. One of those ideas was the rigidity of class distinction, and this was one which waiting in a restaurant fossilized. A waiter is nothing if not a snob. And this outlook nearly ruined his life. It was his first open brush with fate.

Because he felt shy when he talked to her, he did not speak to her outright about himself or ask the normal questions one would of a stranger. Instead he made a few surreptitious inquiries about her from the others. He consulted the class register. The results shocked him. He had noticed, with the ability of fine distinction born of being a waiter, that she spoke with an educated accent. Now he discovered that she lived in one of the better suburbs, that her father had a job in the Civil Service—albeit a minor one—and that she was only studying dressmaking for her own amusement. Inevitably he decided that she was quite beyond his reach. Nothing would have induced him for a moment even to confess that he loved her.

It is a very striking thing that a man may be ambitiously energetic in one direction and lacking all spirit in another. He had met nothing but obstacles in his path when he had set out to be a dress-designer, but he had determined to break them all down. There was, for him, no fence too high to be surmounted. But when he found himself face to face with the barriers of caste, which he regarded as immutable, he was both hopeless and helpless. The barriers could not be pierced. She was one side; he was the other; and there it was.

His mind became distraught. The image of the girl kept floating in front of him. She even came between him and his beloved studies, so that instead of seeing the printed page in front of him he saw only her grey-blue eyes smiling at him. He found his attention in class wandering, his gaze leaving the blackboard, where hitherto it had been riveted, and stealing round to focus itself on that trim chestnut head. The evenings which had been so enjoyable to him grew agonizing. One day, unable to face the situation, he stayed away—the first time he had ever absented himself. He felt he was lost, that every one of his dreams must now fade. Actually it was the best thing he had ever done.

The following week he summoned up his courage and again went to the institute. His heart fluttered as he entered the class-room. He looked round furtively, but she was not there. Still, quite often she was one of the last to arrive; she had a journey to make. And as he stood miserably, unable to make up his mind whether to stay or return home, one of the other young men in the class sidled up to him with a knowing leer. He was a youth—one of the few—with whom Peter had managed to converse on occasions.

"I always thought you were a dark horse," he said in a tone of innuendo. "Been doing a bit on the quiet, eh?"

Peter looked at him blankly.

"I don't understand," he said.

"No?" The leer came again. "That dame Helen—looking everywhere for you last week. Thought you were ill and got quite worked up about it. Well, good luck to you. She's a smart bit of stuff."

The general air of salaciousness passed unnoticed by Peter. His mind was in a whirl. She cares, he thought. She cares! She had missed him! He felt himself going red and he felt confused. He did not even notice the broad grin on the face of his informant.

At that moment she came in. She saw him and stopped. She came towards him. He heard her asking if he had been ill and hoping he was better . . . That evening he changed his place and sat next to her. Wild thoughts were in his mind. He almost failed to realize that it was he himself speaking when he suggested, at the end of the class, that he should walk along the road with her.

She loved him. That evening they became engaged, and from that moment he lived in a whirl of happiness such as he had never believed to be possible.

The effect of love such as this on a man filled with ambition can have just one of two effects. He may either become so consumed with his love that all else seems futile; or he may feel inspired to new efforts even greater than those he had made before. It was the latter effect the new situation had on Peter. He worked with greater enthusiasm than ever. Where, till then, he had merely shown promise and competence, now he grew brilliant. He outstripped the whole of the class. Though he contrived to see as much of Helen as he could, he still found time for his work, because he was now able, it appeared, to do twice as much in a given period.

When, a couple of months later, the course ended, the teacher was so impressed by Peter's progress and keenness that he gave him a special letter of recommendation to a friend in the trade. The result was beyond all Peter's wildest hopes. He found himself with a job in a wholesale sportswear house with a famous name. It was only a junior position in the design department, but it was a real beginning; and the rest lay with his own abilities, which he did not doubt.

Helen had a job of her own, and the two discussed plans with the eagerness of all young lovers. It was Christmas, and they decided that, if Helen remained in her position for the time being, they could get married in June. At last the sun was shining. Everything seemed set for happiness for both of them. Blinded by bright visions, they failed to see the cloud that was banking up and became later so big that it threatened to blot out everything.

It was in March that Peter fell ill. It was the first time in his life that he had ever been forced to take to his bed. Perhaps, as so often happens, it was now when he permitted himself to relax a little that the beginnings of lung-trouble showed themselves. He went to see his doctor, who looked grave and without saying much sent him to a specialist for detailed examination.

The cloud was now black and menacing. The specialist's verdict was that there was a touch of tuberculosis on one lung. He explained to Peter the seriousness of it all, not only to himself but possibly to others.

Peter felt crushed. It was as though he had been lifted to a great height only to be dropped again. What had he done to deserve this terrible blow? Was it a sin to be fired with ambition and to work for its realization? He might be able to carry on with his job, but that now was only part of his life. The other—and greater—part was Helen. What should he do? He pondered the question till his mind reeled. Till then he had been serious in his outlook, but had always been ready for a joke; now he grew morose and depressed. Then, summoning up his courage, he told Helen of his decision: the marriage must be abandoned. She could not marry a sick man. They could not face the risk of bringing tubercular children into the world. Above all he could not face the risk of endangering her.

It was her turn to be heartbroken. Every minute of her day had been spent in making plans for their married life. She had won her parents over, but now they joined forces with Peter. The marriage was impossible and they admired Peter for his frankness and for this expression of his devotion and care for Helen. Yet she herself could not at first see the full force of these arguments. She had not had Peter's grim childhood, nor had she seen, as he had, the terrible toll tuberculosis takes of those whom poverty condemns to live in sunless houses and on a poor diet. It was that experience which enabled him to make the hard decision from which he could not be diverted.

He was incurable. He knew it. He accepted that with the same blind faith as once he had taken for granted that the gulf between Helen and himself was unbridgeable.

Helen had not the same fatalistic attitude as he had. Perhaps the very fact that she had not devoted herself all her life to one burning ambition had given her a wider knowledge, a less ready acceptance of things as they were. She tried to find out all she could about tuberculosis. She read. She talked to friends. And by chance one of these happened to be a nurse. That friend was not at all convinced that Peter's case was hopeless. It was a small spot on one lung. She advised Helen to persuade Peter to come and see me.

Both of them came together. It was she who told me the whole tragic story, she who was making the fight. For Peter himself seemed numb and lifeless. His whole attitude of despair contrasted oddly with that air of alertness and determination that I noticed as soon as I had shaken hands with him. Of course, the reason became plain as the tale unfolded. He was a man with one ambition, and one ambition only. To him the world was dress-designing and though other men had made a living in other mysterious ways, their work was not important. To him, life was no longer worth living.

When they had finished, Helen looked at me with appealing eyes. What could be done? She was sure something could be done. Medicine had advanced so fast and so far of recent years. Was it to be helpless in the one case that mattered?

I looked at Peter. The first thing was to re-arouse his wish to live and show him there was something to live for.

I spoke very seriously.

"The first thing you have to understand is that with proper treatment," I said, "tuberculosis is decidedly not incurable. The only reason so many cases are incurable is that they have been allowed to go too far before the surgeon is called in—but that goes for a good many other diseases, too. Yours isn't such a case. The spot is small, and you can be operated upon. You see, the germ that causes tuberculosis cannot live without air, and so if the affected lung is collapsed and all the air is expelled from it, the germ dies. In a few months, you should be cured."

He looked at me and to my surprise he laughed bitterly.

"I wish I hadn't heard you say that, doctor. You see, I've no doubt all that is correct, but then that sort of operation isn't for people like me. The rich can usually be cured. It's the poor—the people who have to work and need their health all the time—those are the ones that suffer. I couldn't afford an operation, especially one like that. I shall just have to put up with it and hope the end comes quickly."

I looked at him in some astonishment. It was unusual for a man of his age to take so utterly gloomy a view. But he saw all his hopes slipping through his fingers, and the one I had held out was beyond his grasp.

Helen's eyes filled with tears, but her mouth set.

"Is it really expensive, doctor?" she asked. "I've got a little put by—I saved it for our home"—the tears fell quietly—"but I would gladly spend it on this."

"There's no need," I replied. "The question of cost won't come into it. I can arrange that it shall cost you nothing at all."

Peter snarled. "Oh, I know all about that," he said. "I go into a hospital, and I'm put on a table, and a lot of medical students gather round me as though I was a rat or something, and then someone carves me up. I know. I've known too many people die like that."

"I shall perform the operation myself," I said quietly.

"I'm not in the market for charity," he snapped.

I looked at Helen, trying so hard to hide her tears. I looked at his hopeless expression. And my temper left me. I rounded on him so abruptly that he started back in his chair.

"Listen, young man," I said, "it's time you came to your senses. Do you love your fiancée, or don't you?"

"Oh, what's the good of talking about that now?" he growled.

"It seems to me the most important thing to talk about," I returned. "What I'm offering you is a chance to become a fit man again and the chance to marry her with a perfectly clear conscience that you won't be endangering her or any children you may have. I'm offering you a chance to get on in your career—and I know that means a very great deal to you. And all you do is to put up a lot of silly, stupid obstacles and try to persuade us that all you want is to die. Do you think that Helen here"—I let the name slip out quite naturally—"wants to see you die? Do you think she brought you along here just so that you could behave like a mule—and a rather fatheaded one at that? It's no good going about throwing stones at us doctors if you won't give us the chance. You've fought all your life to get the things you wanted, and now just because of some silly pride in you you're prepared to let them all go—and worse than that, you're quite ready it seems to make this girl who loves you thoroughly miserable. You're behaving like a selfish, spoilt child."

For a moment he could not speak; he was too much astounded by my onslaught. And Helen took up the attack.

"You *are* being rather stupid, you know, Peter dear," she said. "Why should you refuse help when it's offered you? But perhaps you don't care for me any more," she added with a small break in her voice.

He stared at her, and for an unhappy moment I thought he was going to break into sobs. But he controlled himself.

"Darling, how could you say a thing like that?" he asked tenderly, apparently forgetting my presence. Then he dropped his head in his hands. "Oh, God! I think I'm going mad."

But we had no mercy on him. We bullied him and we cajoled him till at last he agreed. Then and there, so that there could be no second thoughts for him, we made the preliminary arrangements. I believed that he was not far wrong when he had said he was going mad. The shock was certainly threatening to warp his whole judgment and make him give way hopelessly to despair.

The first thing was to have the most complete X-ray photographs taken of his lungs so that we could locate and define the trouble precisely. These were encouraging. There was only one small patch affected on the right lung, and that had not gone very far. His general physical condition, though all those years of unremitting study and lack of exercise had undermined it a little, was good. There was no reason at all against the thoracoplasty that I proposed; and every reason for me to believe that it would be successful.

Thoracoplasty is a fairly extensive operation and cannot be entered upon at all lightly. One half of the ribs on the affected side have to be excised in order that access may be gained to the damaged lung. The muscles then contract and compress the lung, from which all air is thus expelled; and the lung does not expand to draw in air again. This sounds serious enough, and a serious operation it is; but the proportion of successes is very high, with modern methods; and it has played a very great part in diminishing the number of deaths from the scourge of tuberculosis—the full remedy for which, of course, will come only when we can give everyone in the country his fair share of good living conditions, good food, and, above all, good, clean, fresh air.

The time came when he was admitted to hospital, and the operation was performed. He took it well, though in the best of conditions the recovery is slow and not a little painful. But after three months of constant observation and ceaseless attention, he was well enough to be sent to a country sanatorium, where the things he had never had in his life—sunshine, pure farm food, and sympathy—would do the rest.

It was a long and trying time for him; but perhaps it seemed even longer and more trying for Helen. She was a daily caller at the hospital when he was getting over the operation, eager for every little bit of news, growing depressed when the inevitable fluctuations seemed to indicate a lack of progress, getting elated when there was a solid advance to report. Yet though she was so much affected, I do not think her faith ever wavered. She knew he would pull through.

Something of that faith infected him little by little. At first, he was not, I must confess, a very good patient. The psychological effect of the shock was still on him, and he was very prone to give way to fits of depression and despair, which always retard recovery. But step by step his outlook grew more sanguine till, by the time he left for the country, he was growing eager to return to his work and even discussing wedding plans with Helen.

It is now a little over two months since he was discharged from the sanatorium, fully recovered and with the whole terrible prospect of a tuberculous life wiped out. I entered the fact in my casebook and drew the line which marks the end of a case in my records.

There, I suppose, the matter should have ended. But, as so often happens, it did not. I was reminded of the case only a few days ago. Indeed it was the reminder that set my thoughts racing back to all its details and made me embark upon this story. For in my morning mail was a little square box with a floral design in silver upon it. It contained a sample of their wedding-cake, and a special card on which were the words: "Acknowledging a gratitude we can never express—Peter and Helen".

I cannot keep the cake. But I have put the card among that collection of personal treasures which above all else make a surgeon's life worth while.

XI

A PINT OF DOCTOR'S BLOOD

If I called him a hero to his face he would, I am sure, grow actively resentful. I can think of no man who would like being lionized less. But for all that he is the hero of this story. I am talking of that pleasant young man Dr. Frank Somers, whom I first met professionally on this case, and who I am now proud to number among my personal friends. Frank Somers is, of course, not his real name. Even if the rules of my profession allowed me to use the real name, I should still refrain. At least he will not be able to say—as he very likely would, if my estimate of him is correct—that I have made a fool of him in front of his friends.

Joseph Lyle was one of Frank's patients and he shares the honours with Frank himself. Indeed, the case is indexed in my memory as that of Frank and Joseph. There is in fact a certain amount of similarity between them. Both are young and likeable; and both have in full measure that quality of courage which is among the highest of human virtues.

Joseph Lyle had been married two years when Frank called me in to see him. He was not in the Forces, despite the fact that he was only twenty-eight, for he held a key job in industry, and he could not be spared. It was a job that imposed long hours and immense strain upon him. Young and vital though he was, the strain began to tell, and it was not so very long before he began to complain of chronic weariness and a general feeling of ill health to which it was impossible to put a definite name. That has been by no means uncommon during these past five and a half years. The war brought many unnameable ills, none more insidious than the general malaise which has affected almost everyone.

This, however, was not simply one of those passing periods of depression from which we all have suffered. After a short time, definite physical symptoms began to show themselves. Frank, who is young and alert, suspected that his glands, those regulators of the human system, were out of order and kept a wary eye upon him. Glandular imbalance as doctors call it is the fecund father of a myriad of ills.

The case developed on unpleasant lines. It was not so much that the physical phenomena were unduly painful or distressing, but the general effect was almost disastrous. He started to lose weight, and it was not long before his friends were remarking on his thinness. He had never been a fleshy man, but even so the change in him was most marked. More uncomfortable to him, he began to perspire very profusely at night, and he himself, led on by the easy path of popular diagnosis, began to suspect tuberculosis, though Frank did nothing to encourage this view. It was not something which, at that stage, could be definitely named.

It was, however, the psychological by-products that were most alarming and the most fraught, in these early days, with potential disaster. Normally he was of an even temper, filled with good humour, a man who was roused to anger only with difficulty, yet at the same time he was not weak or unduly easy-going. He had, it seemed, a balanced view of life, though he was not yet thirty. But now he grew more and more difficult to get on with. The slightest out-of-the-way incident roused him to violent passion. After two years of marriage during which he had been in every way a model husband he took to having at first disagreements and then outright quarrels with his wife, who herself began to show signs of nervous strain and weariness.

Frank told him to rest, but he refused. He felt slightly unhappy at being retained in civil life when all his friends had been called up for the Forces, and he was not going to give up unless forced to by sheer necessity. Frank called on his wife and pleaded with her to use her influence with him so that he might be induced to take a rest; otherwise, the doctor felt, the results might be very serious. She agreed to this course reluctantly—not because she did not see the need for Joseph's resting, but because she had come to fear offering any opinion to him, since his temper was so unreliable, and there were times now when she feared actual physical violence.

Her doubts were more than justified. She put the point to him with great tact, and added, as a further inducement, the fact that she herself was beginning to feel the strain. Even that appeal fell not so much on deaf ears as on hostile ones. He stormed and raged and flung out of the room. The rest of that evening was the most unhappy Mrs. Lyle had ever spent in her married life. He refused to speak to her, and even insisted on sleeping on the couch in the living-room rather than share a room with her.

Next morning he set out for work in the usual way, still saying nothing, and snatching his overcoat out of his wife's hands when she tried to help him on with it. He cast a murderous glance at her as he slammed the door behind him.

It was a sinister beginning to the day, and for once the auguries were not wrong. During that day he collapsed at his work, and, after having been examined by his firm's doctor, he was sent home in a car and Frank was called in at once. It was what Frank had secretly suspected, though he had not thought the evidence strong enough to act upon. Joseph was a victim of toxic goitre. His need was urgent, and Frank telephoned to me without further delay. I went at once. There are times when necessity overrides the regular, ordered procedure of the appointment book.

Not only was that a case of toxic goitre; it was in a very advanced state. An immediate operation was demanded, and I did not hesitate to press the urgency of the need when I saw Mrs. Lyle and a little group of friends who had been waiting in the little living-room of the house.

My proposal was that he should be removed to hospital forthwith, but they would not hear of it. They were quite prepared to pay the necessary fees between them, for they wanted to make sure that Joseph had the best individual attention and that I should perform the operation. He must go into a nursing home. We lost no time over that. They readily agreed to the moderate fee I suggested, and, having made some suggestions about immediate care to Frank, I returned to Harley Street and put in train the necessary steps for getting him a bed in a suitable home.

A few days later, after proper preparation, he was on the operating table, and I was able for the first time to obtain a really exhaustive knowledge of the growth. It was going to be more difficult than I had thought, and if success was to be attained a long and difficult procedure would have to be employed. The goitre—which is a tumour of the thyroid gland—was enormous; and since the thyroid is in the immediate neighbourhood of the gullet, great care would have to be exercised if no damage was to be done. The case was complicated by the fact that the patient was in pretty poor condition, as the result of his long period of hard work and indifferent health. When I saw the full extent of the trouble, I admit that my feelings were not so hopeful as they had been.

It took two hours to excise that tumour, perhaps the biggest of its kind with which I have ever had to deal. It demanded delicate work, and I began to feel a little strained towards the end of the operation. But it was done. The actual excision had been successful. What was to follow now?

I was far from sanguine, though I believed there was a chance of pulling him round, and Frank, who had been present at the operation, thought so, too. The danger lies not so much in the operation itself as in the profound shock that so long a procedure gives to the patient. Moreover he had inevitably lost a great deal of blood—a circumstance which was the more regrettable in view of his initially low condition.

When, therefore, the report the next morning told me that his condition was fairly good, bearing in mind all the circumstances, I was pleasurably surprised, and my hopes rose again. A later report on the same day told the same tale, and when I paid a last visit to him before going home to dinner, he seemed in no immediate danger. It looked then as though a start in the right direction had been made.

The following day, however, there was a distinct turn for the worse. His condition grew lower. I went along to the nursing home to confirm that the right measures were being taken, and my examination of him did nothing to restore the hopes I had entertained the day before. The case of Joseph Lyle was one in which I was resigned to an unsuccessful outcome.

It was no surprise, therefore, when that evening I received an urgent call to go to the home to see him. There had been something approaching complete collapse. His pulse was indetectible, and he had relapsed into a state of coma.

Now the usual treatment in such cases nowadays is the injection of blood plasma, which can be assimilated into the reduced blood stream and enrich and reactivate it. Our efforts to inject this life-giving plasma were desperate. Try as we might, we were unsuccessful. Each time the veins congealed, so that our efforts were quite useless. Once or twice we hoped against hope that this attempt, at least, was promising; but a few minutes later, the blood vessels closed again. His system, unable to battle for itself, was rejecting the aid we might have brought it.

The next step was to try whether he would accept stored blood, but once again we failed. Just before midnight I glanced at Frank and the other doctor who was with him. There was no need to speak. Those moments are familiar to every doctor, more's the pity. We could see that the life we had been trying to save was slipping beyond our reach.

Slowly I left the private ward and walked down the stairs towards the waiting-room. There is no grimmer experience in a doctor's life than when he is forced to tell the anxious, waiting friends and relations that they must prepare themselves for the worst. It is something to which one never grows inured. Always there are the same emotions of regret and helplessness, even of cowardice, which urge one to hurry as fast as possible in the opposite direction, into the waiting car, away from it all . . .

As I entered the waiting-room, three pairs of eyes looked up at me, questioningly, searchingly, as though they were trying to read in my face the message that I brought, whether it was one of hope or doom. These three people were not huddled together. They were sitting apart, as though each wanted to have those silent, leaden moments in solitude; yet each was animated by the same haunting fear, the same desperate hope.

In one corner, I saw a small, bent old lady, on whose naturally smiling face was now an expression of utter, tormenting fear. This was his mother. To her had come the vision of a lost son—a son still not at the peak of manhood. In the other far corner was the charming girl his wife. She had forgotten all those terrible times when he had railed at her and quarrelled with her. She remembered only the moments of supreme happiness they had had together, the man she loved and to whom she wished to give the whole of her life.

These two were silent, immobile, statues graven by the hand of tragedy. The third figure was a man, and he came towards me. This was Joseph's brother. There was the same look of fear in his eyes, but it was tempered by the resolution of a strong man not to give way to the worst until he was overpowered. In silence he grasped my hand. Then he spoke in a low, controlled voice.

"I can see by your face, doctor," he said, "that the situation is critical. Please do something—anything. Stop at nothing, if only you can save Joe's life for all of us."

His gaze fell first upon the wife. To my surprise a small, tearful smile flickered for a moment on her face; and then again her terror-stricken eyes fixed themselves on me. The mother dropped her head and hid her face in her handkerchief.

As I had approached that room I had rehearsed what I had to say. The crisis had been passed and there was no hope . . . We had done everything we could, but he was too weak even to accept the help we proffered. There was nothing now but to wait, but the end was inevitable. It was better to know and brace themselves for the shock of what had to come.

I know it would have been hard, but I did not realize how hard. For here before me were three people who cared for nothing but that this man should live. The words I had planned froze on my lips. No, I could not tell them that way. My courage failed, utterly and completely. And then, four words from my prepared speech seemed to float in letters of fire before my eyes. *Everything has been done.* Had it? Of course . . . And yet . . . No, there was one thing else, a chance so remote as to be barely worth taking.

I tried to smile reassuringly, but I am certain that the brother at least saw how forced and false that writhing of the lips was.

"His condition is very, very grave," I said, controlling my voice. "But I think we can detect a very slight sign of improvement. We are doing everything. We are going to try another blood transfusion. I thought you had better know."

"Thank you," he said simply. I dreaded the thought, even more, of having to come back to that room and tell them I had failed after all. Perhaps, I reflected as I mounted the stairs, it would have been kinder to warn them now in more emphatic terms; and I turned to eat my words. But I checked myself. I could not do that. There was still that remote chance which might succeed.

Now I dreaded facing Frank again. He was young and keen. He might well think that I had failed in my duty, that I was weak and sentimental, that I was trying to be kind only to be cruel. But when I told him he nodded sympathetically.

"No," he said, "you couldn't tell them now. He may last some time yet. Who knows?"

And again he turned to the fruitless quest on which he had been engaged when I had re-entered the room: the search for the faint flicker of a pulse in that moribund form.

I had said another blood transfusion, but how was that to be done? The one thing we had not tried had been a transfusion of whole blood. His system might take that when it had refused both plasma and stored blood. But it was nearly one o'clock in the morning. A transfusion of whole blood meant a blood donor. Where was it possible to find one of the right group at that hour?

We consulted the matron, who had remained tirelessly with us, part of the team fighting for Joseph's failing life. She made a few suggestions and then retired to her room to telephone. In an anxiety perhaps even greater than that of those who waited below, we listened to hear her returning footsteps. At last they came. She was in the room. There was no need for her to speak. She had failed. She did not even have to shake her head.

I looked again at that almost lifeless figure in the bed. So his last, outside chance had gone. There was no hope now. I would have to remake my journey, face once more those three pairs of appealing eyes. And then piercing the cloud of my thoughts, came a voice.

"Try me," it said. "He can have a pint of my blood."

I looked up sharply. It was Frank speaking. I was too astonished, too grateful, even to speak. I held out my hand and grasped his warmly. It is not every doctor who is willlng to shed his own blood in a patient's cause.

But there was still much to be done. Would Frank's blood be of the right group? Unless it was, even this generous offer would be useless. To transfuse blood of the wrong group to a patient is to invite almost immediate disaster. I reflected gloomily on the chances that Frank's blood was of a different group. Nothing seemed to me then, in my mood of hopelessness, more probable than that Frank's blood was of a group that would not agree with the patient's.

But we made the test, fearfully, yet at the same time hopefully, and we watched the little drops on the slide. Frank's eyes met mine, and for the first time that night we smiled at each other. The utterly improbable had come about. The two specimens were of the same group. The transfusion could be made.

Now it was Frank's turn to come under my treatment. In the next half hour we drained a pint of his precious blood from him, and then, overcome with weakness, he was sent to bed. And now came the racking moment. In our efforts to make Joseph's system accept the previous transfusions, we had used almost every available vein in the body. But there was one small one left that offered a chance—the last chance that could not be missed, and I made ready with extreme care for the actual transfusion. The vein was on the arm. But that was not the main problem. There still remained the overriding question: would the veins congeal again? Would even this last offer of help be refused by that tired, weak body that had lost all interest in living?

Drop by drop the fluid that meant life or death entered the vein. I have rarely known such moments of anxiety. The first signs were encouraging, but we had grown unwilling to accept these initial suggestions. This weak body might assert itself to say "so much and no more"; and if it did, all would be over.

The dreaded signs did not appear. But we were still unconvinced. If anyone had asked me and I had replied without caution, I think I should still have said I believed in failure.

All night we watched, but nothing but good signs appeared. And at dawn I left him, the corner turned, a life saved.

Now I went again to the waiting-room. Again I faced those eyes. But this time I could meet them squarely. Even as I stood before them, I seemed to feel that faint flicker which was Joseph's returning pulse.

"You may take hope," I said softly. "The transfusion has been successful, and I think the worst is now over. It will be long, and there is still cause for anxiety. But you may hope reasonably."

It was lamely put, but even good news is difficult to impart sometimes.

The brother grasped my hand again, warmly, gratefully. "Thank you, doctor," he said; and there was a catch in his voice. "You have made a wonderful fight for Joseph, and I don't know how we can ever repay you."

They were words I have heard before, but they never fail to fill me with a mixture of glowing satisfaction at having achieved a goal, and embarrassment. But this time I could make a sincere reply.

"There is little to thank me for," I said. "Keep your gratitude for Dr. Somers. But for him, this case would have been a failure."

I tore myself free from them, for they gathered round me and would not let me go. The sun was rising as I dragged myself wearily into my car. I had two patients in that home now, Frank and Joseph, but neither need cause me any more grave concern. The longest odds had proved winning ones.

Never before had the fresh dawn air felt so cool and vitalizing. It brought with it the message of life.

XII

ONE IN A THOUSAND

Perhaps there is no more harrowing case brought to a consulting-room than that of a young human being standing on the threshold of maturity, yet denied, through long ill-health, those joys which are the right of youth. Here stands one who might be full of joy and imparting joy to others, someone who should be meeting life with bright and happy eyes, yet is bent with sadness. Often these suffering youngsters have never known the delights of childhood. They have been sufferers from the moment they left their mother's womb.

There are some crude eugenists who would not permit such child victims of disease and deformity to live out their so-called useless lives. Compassion of the more sentimental kind does indeed often suggest that that would be the wisest course. Yet it is a very difficult question. Medicine marches forward faster than ever, and if these ailing children can be nursed through adolescence, by that time the cure for their condition may have been discovered. It is the old argument for and against euthanasia in a new and different form. The savage parent takes the deformed child into the forest, where it dies either from the attack of wild beasts or from exposure. Have we really in this twentieth century nothing better to offer?

Of course some conditions are absolutely incurable and so far as human foresight can detect must always remain so. The congenital idiot will never be more than a tragic parody of life in a human form. Yet the majority of states carry no such certainty with them. Today they are on the borderline, with the chances of cure or restoration against them. Tomorrow they may be on the sunny side of the dividing line, which shifts ever more in the same direction, leaving the region of the curable greater than that of the incurable. I personally would rather save a young life than an old one which, at best, may linger on as a mere existence.

There was one case that I remember with very great gratitude, for it was my privilege not so much to save a doomed young life as to give to that life the opportunity of knowing fullness for the first time.

By all the laws of probability, Mary was incurable. She was seventeen when she was brought to me, on the very commencement of radiant adulthood. But that was not for her—or so it seemed. The miracle was that she was alive at all. Her ration of sorrow and suffering had been over-generous, and it had begun in her cradle. It was congenital enlarged spleen, a disease that is nearly always fatal in childhood.

We know a lot about the spleen today—far more than when it was made by the ancients the seat of anger in the body. But we still do not know why this morbid enlargement occurs, or even the mechanism that orders the disease. What we do know to our unhappy cost is the price it demands in human life. The spleen is normally only about four inches long and of a dark bluish colour. It is one of the so-called ductless glands which regulate the affairs of the complex system known as the human body. Its special department is the blood stream. In children, it manufactures, as it were, the blood corpuscles that build up their bodies. In the adult, while performing this function, it also destroys old blood corpuscles and regularizes the composition of the blood. No organ is more vital. None is more dangerous when it fails to do its duty.

When it is disordered, it is like Saturn and eats its own children, destroying vast quantities of blood corpuscles, which it does nothing to replace. And so the sufferer becomes anæmic and weak, unable to combat even the mildest form of infection and the ready victim of any bacteria that may attack the body. Children born with deranged spleens nearly always die in infancy, either directly from their condition or from the diesases to which their lack of resistance lays them open. Occasionally, however, by careful nursing and unremitting attention, they survive all the trials of childhood and grow to a shadow of adulthood, but even so the span of their lives rarely exceeds thirty years—and they are always semi-invalids. Their lives are always in the shadow, until they disappear into the last great shadow of all.

Mary had had an enlarged spleen from her birth, but she was now seventeen. That she had reached that age was due to her devoted mother and sister, who had watched over her ever since her first day on earth. She had never mixed with other children. She had never known the joys of play and romping. She could not even run about on her own. School and its companionship had been denied her, but her mother had given her a good grounding at home, and no-one would have suspected that Mary had never been in a schoolroom. And she had never known what it was to be alone. The most exercise she had been allowed was a walk in the garden and on occasion an expedition to the shops near her home, only a few yards away; but even then she was always accompanied.

Perhaps the thing that struck one most about her was her expression. Hers was a face that, if she had led a normal life, would have been beautiful with the joy of living. Her eyes were large and blue, and her lips had that fullness which goes with smiles. Instead, in her blue eyes was melancholy, and her mouth had a sad droop. Her features had the soft contours of youth, yet her whole face suggested ageless suffering, a depth of anguish that was almost beyond human conception.

The war had affected her deeply and added to her perennial depression. War to her meant suffering; that was what she saw above all in it; and she knew enough of suffering to wish it to no-one whoever he might be. The air-raids brought suffering all round her, and added to her own, though she was never a casualty. Nor was that all. Other girls were doing their part in helping, particularly in alleviating the horrors she abhorred. Yet she could do nothing at all. She had nothing but her thoughts.

Her friends left one by one, to join the Wrens, the W.A.A.F. or the A.T.S. and she envied each of them in turn. But she envied most of all those who went into the nursing service, even as ambulance drivers or attendants in Civil Defence. Theirs was the finest job of all, she thought—helping to conquer suffering.

Now she was developing on top of her melancholy an active grudge against life. Often she would say to her mother: "Why did you spend so much trouble on me, Mother. It would have been much better to let me die as a child." And perhaps her mother at times realized there was some truth in the words and tears welled into her eyes.

Ever since she had been old enough to think for herself she had one eternal question on her lips: "Can't I be cured?" And to satisfy her her mother took her to see specialists. She went to one, another, and a third. Their opinion was unanimous: an operation would help, but there was not a chance in a thousand that she would survive it. The argument did not impress Mary, whose long hours of inactive thinking had given her an astonishing, if subjective, grip on life.

"What does it matter?" she asked. "I am barely more than just surviving now. If it succeeded, I should be better. If it did not, then at least I should be spared a few more years of this life which isn't a life."

She knew that her days were numbered, even if the exact extent could not be known. She insisted on seeing one more specialist. Perhaps he would be more venturesome. Perhaps he would be, as she thought, more humane, and open the door to death even if he could not unlock the door to life.

So it was that she was brought to see me. I was interested in her, not merely as a case, but as a personality. There was something alert and intelligent about the girl, a depth to her character that I found very fascinating. And so, before examining her in detail, I talked to her. We talked for an hour, and I gained an insight into a live, inquisitive mind, yet also a mind that was shadowed over with suffering. If she had been a little less acute, she might have suffered less. But then it is always those who are the more sensitive who can touch the heights of sorrow as they can attain the peaks of pleasure.

The examination which followed was astounding. An enlarged spleen it was obvious I should find. I had not the slightest suspicion that I might find the opinions of others entirely wrong. But I had not expected to discover such an enormous enlargement. As I have said, the spleen is normally about four inches in length, but hers now occupied almost the whole of the abdominal cavity. I could scarcely believe my own judgment, and I re-examined her just to confirm my own doubts. No, the incredible thing was that she still lived.

The other surgeons had said it was a chance in a thousand. That was putting it at its lowest. Yet there was that chance, and a chance seen and recognized cannot be ignored. I sent her away and said I would think over her case.

At last I decided that it was worth taking the chance. Mary was too rare a spirit to be denied some attempt on her behalf. I asked her mother to call and told her and explained the position. I did nothing to minimize the danger. If it had been possible, I should have exaggerated it, and still fought for the chance. But it was impossible to do that. The plain statement of the facts was enough.

Mary's mother took a great deal of persuading, I think she felt that to risk this operation was to set at naught all she had done in caring so long for her daughter. It was throwing away the work of years. But I pressed its urgency.

"The choice has to be made now," I said. "Mary's spleen is incredibly big, and in any event she is likely to die very soon. Are you ready to deny her the one chance of living on—and, if it is successful, it would mean not merely a continuance of her present existence but a much fuller, more active, and happy life."

I could see that my appeal weakened her resistance and I pressed home my advantage.

"You have saved her so far in a miraculous way," I said. "Few mothers would have done so much so skilfully. Here is the opportunity to see your work crowned with real success. Otherwise, you will have to face the end you have dreaded and fought against all these years. Put it this way: your choice lies between giving Mary a chance to live with the odds in favour of death, on the one hand; on the other certain death very soon, without any chances in favour of life. I know it is a horrible decision for any mother to have to make, yet you have to make it. You cannot blind yourself with the belief that if all is left alone she will go on from year to year as she is now. If I seem cruel in saying this, it is because I think you should have all the facts put before you."

"I must have time to think it over," she said rather miserably.

"I don't wish you to make a rush decision," I returned, "but this must not be left a day longer than necessary."

She nodded and left me, after a few more words.

When I was alone again, I felt that I had brought her to my way of thinking. I knew Mary would be on my side. But reviewing the whole proposal in cold blood, I must confess my courage quailed a little. The risks were, in truth, enormous, and it would be little short of a miracle if any sort of success was gained. For all that, I did genuinely believe that the attempt was worth making.

It was less than two hours later when the mother telephoned to say she had discussed it with Mary and her sister and was now quite ready to agree to the operation. I decided to act at once. That evening, Mary was in the hospital. The great adventure had begun.

The operation itself was going to be difficult enough, but that was not the biggest anxiety. The risk lay almost entirely in Mary's condition. For years she had been starved of blood, and her anæmia was very bad indeed. In a normal person, there are between four and five million red corpuscles in every small drop of blood. But Mary's blood contained barely a third of that number. In her present condition, not merely a major operation, but almost any intervention that would involve loss of blood, was unthinkable. The only course was to endeavour to make good the deficiency by transfusion.

For two long weeks, therefore, she was given blood transfusions on alternate days. It was a hard and bitter fight with the diseased spleen, which destroyed the new blood as fast or nearly as fast as it was introduced into Mary's system. But the more it destroyed, the more blood she was given, until at last it was clear that we were getting the upper hand. This was a reassuring sign. The first stage had been gained. Mary was now in a fairly reasonable condition to stand the operation. I kept her under observation for a little longer, to make sure that her new condition had become as stabilized as could be expected, and then, as it was important no time should be lost, I made arrangements for the operation.

It was an almost terrifying task, and it was clear that my assistant regarded it as practically hopeless. For three hours, Mary was kept alive on the table by continuous blood transfusion, for only by this means was the intervention possible at all. And the actual removal of the gigantic spleen presented quite enough technical difficulties in itself. It was a real ordeal, and I have rarely felt so glad when an operation was over as I felt then. There were moments when I almost despaired of attaining the immediate end of performing the operation successfully. The spleen was even bigger than I had supposed. Without exaggeration it weighed a good twelve pounds—it would have made a good museum specimen.

Now came the real battle. Could Mary overcome the shock of that prolonged operation? For many days the issue was in doubt, with the probabilities weighted on the side of failure. For ten of those days she was kept on continuous blood transfusion, since she was unable to provide the vital blood from her own system.

Her mother was there all the time, anxious, patient, fearful. Sometimes when I spoke to her she seemed to have a look of accusation in her eyes as though she believed that I was robbing her of the child on whom so much care had been spent. Perhaps she suspected that in the cause of science I had carried out an experiment the results of which might bring nothing but sorrow to her, whatever humanity at large might learn from it. She never spoke of it, however, and it may be that, in my own anxiety over the case, I saw in the mother's eyes only a reflection of the doubts and misgivings to which I myself was subject from time to time. Yet the reaction would have been natural, and on balance I do not think I was altogether mistaken in my belief. I do not grudge her those doubts if she had them. To her, the state of her child must have appeared utterly hopeless. I had to all intents and purposes destroyed even the shadowy life that Mary had hitherto possessed and replaced it by a sort of mechanical process in which Mary was little different from the immortal chicken's heart in Alexis Carrel's laboratory.

Above all the worries and trials of those anxious days I remember a day in Spring, 1942. It was some time after the operation. For the first time, Mary was being allowed to see the outside world. The blinds of her room had been slightly drawn back and a beautiful ray of sunshine struck across the room and fell upon the bed. It was a symbol of hope fulfilled. That was the first day on which we were convinced that Mary would live, and that the initial and most important stage of the battle had been won.

Now there were other questions to face, and I did not know the answers. I barely dared even to guess at them. There was little doubt that she would live now and probably attain a full tale of years. But what would those years be? Would she recover to something like normality, or would the rest of her life be spent in a form of invalidism little different from that which had gone before? Only time could give the solution of those problems. All of us had to wait as patiently as we could. For those of us who were in attendance on her, there was the relief provided by the active work of rebuilding her strength and making provision for the various emergencies that might arise. For her mother there was little but quiet watching and waiting. Often it is the patient's closest friends who have the greater ordeal to endure. They feel helpless when their overwhelming wish is to give all they have. They can do nothing. They may not even give way to the justifiable doubts and worry they experience, lest they communicate these things to the patient and retard recovery. I never cease to admire their unfailing faith and trust and patience, which often make me feel humble.

What shall I say of Mary's ultimate recovery? It is almost impossible to describe, for it seems like a fairy tale come true, the story of a young and beautiful princess released at last from the enchantment under which she had been placed by a wicked sorcerer when she was in the cradle. She left the hospital after two months of careful nursing, and even then I would have retained her longer but for the fact that I knew she would receive such good care at home at the hands of a mother who had already shown herself a devoted and intelligent nurse. She was weak—but she was whole.

Step by step she did not so much win back her strength as build up a strength and health she had never known before. She did not resume the guise of the frail girl whose every movement had to be watched, but grew gradually into young womanhood. The physical change was extensive enough, but it brought with it psychological adjustments that must have been perplexing and at times alarming to her. She now found she could move about like other girls; she could even indulge in sports. It was no longer necessary for her to be attended every time she went on a short walk. All this meant acquiring the technique of a new way of life—a technique that others of her age had developed naturally and gradually from the days of their childhood.

I last saw Mary sitting in her garden. We talked for a little while and then she said she was going to fetch me some tea. I demurred, not merely from politeness, but because I felt she should not exert herself. But she insisted, and a little while later returned bearing a tray loaded with cups and saucers and cake dishes, carrying it with ease and confidence. It was difficult to imagine that this was the same girl as I had seen lying on a bed, her fitful life not so much her own as the product of the blood pumped into her from outside.

Yes, that was the last time I saw Mary, though I hope one day to see her again. But in May, 1944, her mother came to see me. She, too, was a different woman. A load of care had been lifted from her; for the first time in her life since Mary had been born, she was able to enjoy herself wholeheartedly and give her full attention to her own affairs and those of her family at large. The strain of tending Mary had been immense though she had barely realized it. She had denied herself this and that and had come to accept this life of sacrifice as normal. But all that was over. She had been to a matinée the day she came to see me—the first time she had ventured to a theatre for many years, and she was as pleased as a child who has seen its first pantomime.

Of course we talked about Mary, and the one-in-a-thousand chance that had been so successful against every possible probability.

"I haven't seen her for quite a time, you know," her mother said. "But from her letters she is very happy."

"She's away then?" I asked.

Her mother smiled.

"Oh, she's been away for quite a long time now. She joined the Wrens with one of her friends, and she's on radio work, which she likes so much she says she's going to keep it up after the war. Of course, they haven't had any leave for some months, with this invasion hanging about, and she can't say much in her letters."

I was astonished. This was a brighter crown of success than I had expected.

"Yes," her mother went on with a sigh, "it seems absolutely incredible. Three years ago she could barely move, and now she's doing that . . . It's like some miracle story, but then life is always stranger than fiction, isn't it?"

She will be coming back to civilian life again soon, I am told—a bright, fit young woman with the whole of life before her. I turned the leaves of my casebook and ran through the record of her case. Viewed at this distance, and free of the emotional entanglements of the time, I can agree that I must have looked utterly reckless to my colleagues, for if ever there was a hopeless case it was hers. Yet is not that word "hopeless" the one word that a doctor should rule out from his vocabulary? Is it not his duty to seize the most intangible chance and try to turn it into reality? I believe so. More than that I believe it is his duty.

XIII

ONLY TWINS

There is to my mind no greater tragedy in life than that of young parents who, greatly desiring children, yet find themselves unable to have them. Sometimes—very often, in fact, though it is not commonly realized—it is the man at fault; but when the woman fails usually it is more noticeable. She may have successive miscarriages, for example, or her inability ever to bear a child for anatomical reasons is much more apparent than the obscure causes of infertility in the male.

Now I am not a gynaecologist or obstetrician, as I have sometimes been reminded to my cost. But for all that cases of this kind sometimes find their way to me, and for one reason or another—sometimes at the call of personal friendship—I accept them. Most of them have no special features to record outside their purely technical interest, but there is one case which came to me and engraved itself on my memory.

Lila was an Australian girl who had come to this country with her husband on some war mission or other and was remaining here for the duration. She was a small, lively little thing, not perhaps pretty but with a face made highly attractive by its expression of animation. Five years of married life had failed to bring her the child she wanted, and she had taken the wise course, in view of this circumstance, of consulting her doctor. He had had only too unfortunate an experience of her trouble and told her she would be unwise to make any more attempts at child-bearing.

No one could say that she was sterile. In those five years she had had three pregnancies, and in the early months development had been quite normal, but in the third month, as a rule, she became subject to abnormal and very distressing pain, and the upshot was a miscarriage.

Still determined after three disasters that would have turned many women from the very thought of motherhood, she conceived again. Once more the dreaded symptoms appeared in the third month. There was pain and haemorrhage and the doctor was urgently called. There was little he could do beyond giving her some morphine, and then let affairs take their course. Accordingly he promised to call the next day when, he believed, it would be all over in the familiar, tragic way.

Lila, however, was not going to accept that again if there was a way out. She fell to sobbing and despair, but she did not lose her determination. Somewhere, she believed, there must be a doctor who could help her, and she posed the question to a young cousin who had been called in to be with her in her distress.

It is at this point that I make my entry in this story. That cousin had recently been a patient of mine, and she mentioned my name as that of the only specialist with whom she had any direct dealings. Lila did not let the opportunity escape her. She commanded her cousin to telephone me and ask if I could see her at once.

When I heard what was wanted of me, I was not particularly interested.

"I am not a gynaecologist," I said. "You want a specialist in that field. I am a general surgeon."

But the caller would not be fobbed off, and eventually I agreed to call at her house that afternoon. I do not know why, unless it was that the tale of so many miscarriages and of the determination of the would-be mother called to those sentimental deeps which are one of the heritages of my Russian ancestry. The fact remains that almost against my judgment, I went.

When I arrived Lila was in great pain, and the haemorrhage was acute. The morphine was relieving her, but that was all. She was quite lively enough, however, to beg me to do something for her, and she had obviously, for what reason I do not know, an almost childlike belief in my powers of helping her to realize her dreams.

What could be done? As things were a miscarriage was imminent. Perhaps the wisest course would have been to let the miscarriage occur and then to subject her to a very thorough examination to find out the cause of these erratic performances. But that had drawbacks. The result of a fourth disaster might well turn her at last against further attempts at motherhood and have untoward psychological results. If it was possible, the child she had at present in her womb should be saved.

There was Vitamin E, I thought. It is one of the more recently discovered of the vitamins, and its function in the female human being is to aid childbirth. There is no more powerful friend of infants than this vitamin, which is extracted from certain cereal oils; and equally there is no more threatening danger than its absence. I strongly suspected that Lila was deficient in this vital substance.

The question was, however, whether it could be given to her at this late stage, when things had gone so far and she was bleeding profusely. It seemed almost like calling in the fire engine only when the whole building was so far ablaze that it was on the point of collapse. But after a little reflection I decided it might as well be tried. At the worst it would do her no harm; at the best it might save the child.

The method of administration was by injection direct into the bloodstream, but even when I was making the syringe ready I wondered whether it was not too late. The dosage was to be high. I made the injection and waited. The result was almost like magic. The haemorrhage stopped. I could scarcely believe my eyes at these signs of success.

Next day the pains re-occurred with great violence, and I feared that all had been in vain, but there was no miscarriage, and after a little normality returned.

This was all very encouraging, but I decided that it would be foolish to assume that, as one fence had been successfully negotiated, there would not be others in the path. Arrangements were therefore made to have Lila kept under the closest observation, while continuing the treatment by high dosage of Vitamin E. I had the uneasy feeling that we were far from out of the wood yet.

Lila herself had few doubts now, and she was absurdly grateful to me, not knowing, of course, that my treatment had been almost in the nature of an experiment. Her belief was that as that dreaded third month had passed, all would now be well. But I continued to advise her of the need for caution, and I insisted that the vitamin treatment must be continued.

The fifth month came and the baby was still alive. There were no signs at all of any abnormality. The sixth month passed successfully, as did the seventh. It was in the eighth that danger signals again began to appear.

Now she was in very great distress. She grew enormously distended, and—most ominous sign—her heart and kidneys began to show indications of weariness, which are very dangerous pointers. It was difficult to know then how to act. Of course, a premature birth could have been induced, but then the whole of our efforts would have been wasted. If the child was to survive, a little more time must be allowed to elapse.

The wisest course was to have an X-ray photograph taken in order to get a better idea of what was happening, and as soon as the prints reached me I saw that another very startling complication was involved. I thought I had been fighting for one child's life, but the prints showed clearly that Lila had conceived twins. The chances of ultimate success looked smaller now, and indeed it looked as though I should be faced with the problem that is one of the most harassing of all the many in medicine: the choice between the life of the mother and that of her offspring. I wanted to save both, but I had very grave doubts whether it was possible.

Still, there was ample warning in advance, and plans could be made. Lila was removed at once to the hospital, and the theatre was kept in constant readiness for an operation in case of her life being endangered suddenly. For I myself had no doubts now of the course I should choose if the problem arose. It must be Lila's life, not the unborn children's, that must be saved. In any event it was probable that the embryos themselves might die if we waited much longer.

Yet it was a risk we had to take. Time and again she looked at me appealingly and begged me to save her children. Having gone so far and endured so much, they were now more precious to her than ever. The mere idea of having the realization of her dreams almost in her grasp and then having to let it go was too much for her. Though I felt that we could now be sure of saving her life if the worst befell I was more worried than ever by the possible psychological effects of failure. It was my opinion that they might reduce her to a very bad condition that would effect her whole life.

Those were anxious moments, those days of waiting for a threat that did not seem to develop. The course of the case was unpredictable both in regard to form and in regard to time. Danger might not come at all, but if it did, then it might come quickly or build up slowly. Our observations were made closer and even more continuous. Lila was watched with the closest attention till I think she felt she was already in a madhouse, despite the sympathy and tact of the nurses concerned.

It was early in the ninth month of the pregnancy that I decided it would be folly to wait any longer, and three weeks before the normal time I made preparation for a Caesarean section. This would ensure that at least one of the children would be born alive, though it was more than unlikely that the other would be; for while the first was being taken from the womb, the second would be asphyxiated or even drowned in its mother's blood.

That is one of the fastest operations I have ever done. Speed was absolutely essential if success was to be won. Within ten minutes I had extricated the first child alive. So far, so good, it was a great gain from all points of view. My thoughts were moving swiftly. Why should I not try my luck and attempt to save the other one as well? I always like to turn a success into a real triumph, and I moved with celerity. Without waiting to sever the cord of the first child,

I took hold of the second and extricated it from the womb.

It lived. The miracle had happened again. Where under the most favourable circumstances we had expected to see one living child, we now had two. It was an astonishing and gratifying outcome to a case that for months had given nothing but anxiety coupled with that most depressing of all feelings: that all one's trouble was being expended to no good purpose. There was no stage of the case at which I would have given an unqualified affirmative to a question asking me if I thought success probable.

Lila herself made a rapid recovery, and both the children did well. They are girls and identical twins, so that they had to have distinguishing marks put upon them, for they are quite indistinguishable apart. Lila looked at me with happy eyes when she was well enough to talk again.

"Thank you—oh, I can never thank you enough," she cried. "I never thought that it would be possible, after all those failures! And twins! I always wanted twins. I think they're marvellous."

"I'm glad," I said, "but you gave us some very trying moments, you know. Perhaps these twins will keep you out of mischief for some time to come. It's come off this time, but it was touch and go, and you mustn't think it can happen every time with your bad record. Besides, the strain wouldn't be at all good for you."

She smiled. "No," she said. "That's why I'm so glad they're twins. I don't think I could face all that over again—or even anything like it. And now I've got two. You see, I've never believed in only children. I don't think it's fair to them having to grow up alone as they do. And now I've got two, I shan't be tempted to try to provide a playmate for the first." She smiled again.

"I'm very glad you take that sensible view," I replied. "If ever you do think you'd like another, you'd better be thoroughly examined first by a specialist and put under proper treatment from the first. You just can't afford to take any more risks."

"Yes, I think I'd do that. Of course, I should come to see you. You've been so wonderful."

I shook my head very decidedly. "No, young lady," I said firmly. "That's all very well, but you and your cousin bullied me into taking your case, and I don't think I should do it again. I can't guarantee to work miracles to order or bring off a thing like this a second time. Besides, as I told you right at the start, I am not a gynæcologist. After my experience with you I'm quite sure I don't want to be one. The trials and troubles of a general surgeon's life are quite enough for me, and I don't want to add to them unnecessarily."

She listened attentively and seriously to this rather over-long and emphatic speech. Then she smiled again, more broadly than before.

"All the same," she said softly. "I shall come when it's necessary."

XIV

NEW EYES

There is no more horrible affliction than blindness. It cuts off man from the use of that sense which gives him his greatest pleasure and experience. With the exception of his near relations the great apes, some insects and some birds, man is the only animal that has the ability to distinguish colours clearly, and to appreciate their infinite subtlety. A man who has been cut off from the sight of the flowers coming to bloom once more in the spring, who has never seen the sea or the dim darkness of a great forest, who has been denied enjoying the majestic sight of great mountains, who has never seen a child or a lovely woman smile—such a man can never have really lived, however successful he may be in going about his daily affairs. It is true that the blind develop greater acuteness of hearing, so that the sounds of the world mean more to them; their fingers and indeed their whole bodies have a much more sensitive power of touch. But these can never replace those sightless eyes, and it is sheer sentimentality to try and pretend that they can.

The blind man, too, is to a surgeon a living reproach. There is nothing that can be done for him. One can give the victim of an accident new arms and new legs; one can rebuild his face or straighten a crooked limb. But there is nothing to be done for the blind man. His eyes have gone. They can never return.

At least, that was the state of affairs until comparatively recently. But in the past few years some success has been won in surgery of the eye, and it was my very great privilege to be concerned with a case in which this new technique, which may mean so very much for the benefit and happiness of humanity, was used.

It was a particularly tragic case, for it was that of a child, a little girl named Barbara. She was only five years of age, and she was full of high spirits. Though so young she already had acquired the reputation of falling into mischief whenever the chance was there, but not through naughtiness—she was in every way a charming child. Her only trouble was an excess of boisterous fun.

One day she went to visit some cousins of hers, much about the same age as she, and they started to play hide-and-seek and other games in the nursery. And because Barbara was there, these pastimes developed a joyousness that is often absent from them. And it was in one of the ensuing scrambles that the accident occurred.

There was an open fire in the nursery, and by some mischance it was not protected by a fireguard. She was pushed towards the fire, tried to recover, and pitched face forwards onto the living coals. It was lucky her aunt, the cousins' mother, came in at that moment. Barbara was dragged off, screaming horribly, but before any deep-seated damage could be done.

At least, that was how it seemed. The aunt acted with the greatest promptitude. I think she had had some training in first aid, for she covered the burns with dry dressings and did not risk making them worse with the various lotions and ointments so many people use unwisely, and then brought the little girl straight to hospital. It so happened that I was the surgeon who handled the case, and it led me into a very interesting experience.

I was staggered when I examined her. It was quite true that the burns themselves were not very bad burns. They were nothing to the terrible injuries I had seen and handled as the results of flying accidents. The face itself would heal well, and any subsequent plastic corrections could be easily made. But these burns, the most obvious ones, were not alone; nor were they the most serious. Her eyes were affected.

Deeply shocked, I examined her eyes very closely. There was no doubt about it. The cornea, the outer transparent part of the eye, had been very badly damaged. I feared the worst, especially as there was nothing that could be done about it.

As the days went by, the position became even more tragically plain. The burns on her face healed quickly and healthily. So did the burns on her eyes, but here it was the very act of healing that destroyed the sight. For as the damaged tissues rebuilt themselves they formed a thick scar; and it was this scar which blacked-out her vision. The rest of her eye and optic nerves were as healthy as they had ever been.

It saddened me as it had so often before that here in front of me was one of the cases that are beyond human skill. By a sad mischance she had lost her most precious possession, and no amount of argument could get rid of that horrible fact.

I was to see quite a lot of Barbara in the next few weeks, for at her parents' request I was undertaking plastic treatment to make good the slight damage left by the burns on her face. I had to graft new eyelids and also graft a new piece of skin into the centre of the forehead. That I was able to do this and still be incapable of doing anything for those sightless eyes depressed me each time I saw her.

My own particular work did not prove at all troublesome. The skin grafts occupied three separate operations, and by the end of three months Barbara's appearance was normal again. If she slept or closed her eyes she was the beautiful child she had been before the accident. It was only when she opened her eyes that one realized she was blind. The appearance of the eyes was bad enough, but perhaps the most heart-rending circumstance was the fact that this child had that fixed, sightless stare which all the blind have, as though they are trying to force apart, by sheer willpower, the curtains that close them in.

The effect on the child was, not unnaturally disastrous. She lost all those high spirits which had previously marked everything she did. She showed little interest in anything. Her life, which had been filled with happiness, now became a continued twilight of melancholy. She had lost the world which she was beginning to know so well, and she had not the mental storehouse of memories on which those who go blind at a later age could draw.

Her parents were almost distracted. The idea of their beloved daughter's going through life absolutely blind filled them with agony. They tried to draw cold comfort from the thought that, being young, she might be able to educate herself to a world of perpetual darkness, but it brought them no relief.

Again and again they came to me and importuned me to do something. But I had to shake my head and return a refusal.

"There is nothing I would more gladly do if it were possible," I said. "But to start with I am not an ophthalmic surgeon—and the eye is a highly specialized piece of human mechanism. Add to that, that there is really nothing to be done. It's cases like these," I went on bitterly, "that make one realize how very far we have still to go, and that the rapid progress of the last few years hasn't taken us as far as we thought it had."

They tried again. Surely modern surgery was not as hopeless as that, they asked. I had to confess that it was.

When the operations on Barbara had been finished, they came once more—this time to thank me. They expressed their pleasure and gratitude for what I had done, but I could feel that the thought uppermost in their minds was one of disappointment. I could imagine that they were asking themselves if the plastic operations I had performed were of any real use, and I am certain they would rather have seen their little daughter scarred for life if only it had been possible to save her sight.

It was a depressing end to a tragic case and it was on my mind for quite a time. Again and again I asked myself, as they had asked me, if nothing could be done. It certainly did seem most unsatisfactory, to say the least, to leave things as they were. Of course, I knew that in Russia there had been operations for which success had been claimed in grafting cornea, but the technique had not been fully described, and one is apt to discount first reports of new procedures—as of new drugs—from all countries. Too often subsequent experience proves that the initial claims were too sweeping.

And then as if in answer to my question I happened upon an article in a recent issue of an American medical journal, dealing in great detail with an operation for grafting a healthy cornea from another person under conditions very similar to those of Barbara's case, and its success had been undoubted. I read it through again carefully and compared it with what I had gathered about the work in Russia. The whole secret of success was that the grafted cornea should be fresh—taken either from a living person surrendering it voluntarily or from someone who had died, in which case the cornea had to be removed immediately after death.

Here at least was a chance—one of those chances which, I admit, I like to take when the prize is human happiness. But I knew I had not the specialized skill to perform that operation myself. Accordingly I put the journal in my pocket and went straight to a friend of mine, a well-known ophthalmologist. I asked him if he knew of this procedure and what he thought of it.

He smiled.

"My dear George," he said, "I've known about that for some time, and as to my opinion of it—well, I can only say that ever since I first investigated it I've been longing for a chance to perform it."

"I think I can give you the chance you want," I replied.

"Eh?" he said sharply, sitting up in his chair. "Tell me about it. I'm all ears."

"No," I returned firmly. "Come and see for yourself."

I could see he was interested—very much so; but he pleaded that he had work to do and could not come at that moment. I was adamant. I would not let him go; and though I almost dragged him to the car and bundled him into it, I knew that he was, in reality, far from reluctant. As a matter of fact, he was filled with the liveliest curiosity.

I relented to the extent of telling him something of the case as we drove to the hospital where Barbara was. She was still under observation though the case was, to all intents and purposes, over. His eyes grew thoughtful.

"It sounds all right," he said at length. "But of course it needs almost ideal conditions. First of all the eyes themselves must be healthy, or you'll only make bad worse, and the graft won't take. And then all the nerves must be perfectly healthy. The main difficulty is then to get hold of the cornea for the graft. It isn't everyone who'll give it up, and fresh cadavers aren't too easy to get hold of."

"We shall have to see," I said non-committally. I had the feeling that as my luck had run strong so far, it would not desert me now. If the operation was technically possible, the material means could be found somehow.

His examination of Barbara was very thorough, but I had little doubt of its outcome. Eventually he looked at me with an eager smile.

"Yes, there's no special difficulty there," he said. "There's rather more than a chance. Now, I suppose, we start the really sticky business—parents' consent, finding a cornea, and the rest."

"I don't expect much opposition from the parents," I returned. "As a matter of fact they've seen me several times and implored me, almost on bended knees, to do something about it. I wish I'd consulted you sooner."

"You should have. But still there's no particular loss."

I telephoned Barbara's parents and said I wanted to see them at once, and to bring a specialist friend with me. Though I was no more definite than that, I think they guessed what it was about, for they told me I could come whenever I liked, and I learnt afterwards that they had postponed a dinner engagement to receive us.

First of all I introduced my friend and told them who he was, and then I left it to him to explain the operation and the chances of success. Their eyes sparkled with hope.

"But this is wonderful!" the mother cried. "I always believed you'd find some way out, Mr. Sava, in spite of all your pessimism. I didn't believe that surgery was quite as bankrupt as you tried to make out. When can it be done?" she asked, turning to my friend.

"That's the whole difficulty," he said. "We can never tell. The only thing I can see is that we must wait for an accident fatality, or a death in the hospital, and get the relatives' permission to excise a portion of the cornea for grafting. I can't see any other way."

"I don't think I like that idea," she remarked slowly. I expected the usual objections about making use of dead men's tissues, but that was not in her mind. "In a way," she went on, "the anxiety of waiting, knowing that something can be done and we've got to wait till circumstances make it possible would be worse than trying to resign oneself to the knowledge that it's hopeless. Besides, I don't see that it's necessary."

"Not necessary?" asked my friend, looking at her keenly.

"No," she replied calmly. "You've explained it all very clearly, and you've said that it isn't necessary to take a piece from a dead body. You can take a piece of the eye of a living person. I believe my eyes are quite healthy, and I would gladly give them for Barbara's sake, poor little mite. I'm starting to get old"—I smiled; she was barely thirty-five —"and she's got all her life in front of her. I suppose it would be all right."

"That's really magnificent of you," said my friend seriously. "But you realize what it would mean? You will probably lose the sight of one eye."

"That is better than having Barbara completely blind. I should be able to see a bit. In any event my oculist tells me I have a lazy eye, so I don't suppose it would make much difference." She laughed softly.

I was astonished at her courage, which filled me with admiration. Here was a mother indeed. She was not merely prepared to make any sacrifice for the sake of her daughter; she was happy to do so. It confirmed the belief I have always held that in some things at least, women are more courageous than men, because they have the power of unselfishness developed to a higher degree.

Then and there, my friend fetched his bag and made a preliminary examination of her eyes. At the end of it he pronounced himself satisfied, but he asked her to come along to his consulting-rooms the next day so that he could make a fuller examination. I was to be present so that the necessary arrangements could be made.

So the day came, that same week, for the actual operation. It was, for me, a thrilling experience, for I have never witnessed a more wonderful piece of work in my life. Its delicacy astonished me, used though I am to these things, and I marvelled at the sure and refined technique of my friend.

First of all, using a specially made instrument, he excised a piece of scarred cornea from Barbara's eye. It was no more than a tenth of an inch square and to remove it so exactly required the skill of a first-class instrument maker—with the difference that the ophthalmologist was working in a much less malleable material than metal. The next step was to cut a piece exactly similar from the eye of the mother. This demanded an even more refined technique to ensure that there was complete identity. This new piece was then fitted into the space left in the child's cornea. At every stage, the slightest slip would have ruined the whole operation, and it was incredible that my friend had never actually performed this operation before.

The graft took well, and in a few weeks' time my friend decided it was safe to embark upon the work on the other eye. Once again that delicate excision and matching was carried out; and once again the results proved highly satisfactory.

As we drove away after the completion of the second operation, my friend looked soberly at me.

"I've got to thank you, George," he said, "for letting me have this opportunity. It's been a grand experience, and I think we are going to do big things with it in the future."

"Yes," I returned. "It's almost miraculous and makes my bread-and-butter work look like sheer plumbing. As a matter of fact I was going to thank you for giving me the privilege of seeing it."

He chuckled. "What is this?" he asked. "A mutual back-slapping society? Let's cut it out. As a matter of fact, the most remarkable thing about it is the behaviour of the mother. She's absolutely splendid. If I'd said she was sure to go stone blind she'd still have insisted on giving herself as a donor. It's wonderful what some women will do."

"What about her?" I said. "Will she be able to see moderately well?"

"I think so," he replied. "I shall do my best. She deserves at least as much attention as the child."

I agreed with him.

His prophecy turned out to be correct. There was sufficient cornea left on the mother's eye to enable her to retain her vision, though it is now not nearly so good as it was. She has to wear glasses, but she does not regard that as a drawback in the circumstances. It is, in fact, difficult to decide which she admires most: the skill of my friend in restoring sight to Barbara or his care in preserving her own eyes. Barbara, too, has to wear glasses and probably will all her life. But that again is better than the sightless, joyless life to which she seemed condemned but for this miraculous operation.

It is not merely her sight that has been restored. As soon as she began to see again and get about, her natural high spirits began to return. Where she had been dull and listless, she was now boisterously full of life. The only handicap she found was the spectacles, but good fitting of the frames reduced that disadvantage to a minimum. I visited her mother and father a little while ago. They spoke to me with sincere gratitude of the work my friend and I had done for them, but I turned all the credit to him. After all I had been extremely stupid in not consulting him at once. I might never have chanced on that article in the American journal, and Barbara might still have been pathetically blind . . .

As I was thinking thus, there was a crash in an upstairs room. It was so sudden and unexpected that I could not help looking up sharply. The mother smiled.

"That's only Barbara," she remarked. "She loves throwing things about, and I expect that's one of the nursery chairs going through it again. They suffer a lot these days, but we like hearing the noise about the place. You see," she went on seriously, "it might have been so different. The only sounds we heard might have been those she made when she knocked things over because she could not see them."

She sighed and then she held out her hand to me. I grasped it in silence.

XV

POWERFUL JAW

In the heyday of gangsterdom in Chicago, some of the leaders were reputed to have their own plastic surgeons in their entourage for the purpose of altering their features to prevent recognition. I do not know whether this is true or not, but even if it was, the alterations were not likely to attain the desired end. An experienced detective is far more likely to recognize a man by his walk and the set of his shoulders as seen from the back than by his features, which can be readily disguised; for those two characteristics are practically impossible for a man to change.

Of course, a plastic surgeon can alter a person's features very considerably. A large amount of his work, in fact, consists in doing precisely that thing. It is surprising how the removal of even a small scar from a person's face seems to alter it completely, and as it is usually accompanied by a change in expression, due to the relief of psychological tensions, the result is very often an entirely new face. So simple a thing as fitting a set of false teeth can produce equally striking results by filling out the sunken cheeks and averting the drawn-in lips once more—which is why so many people are told that their dentures do not suit them.

Many people come to the plastic surgeon to have their features changed not simply out of vanity but to enable them to overcome real difficulties. I can never stress the psychological side of such plastic operations too much; to my mind they will always be the most important of all. I have told elsewhere of women who have become morbidly self-conscious because of some abnormality in their appearance, but men, too, quite frequently find it necessary to have plastic operations performed because their appearance is a definite handicap.

I am not now thinking of war injuries, accident cases, and so on. Those come into a different category. Here the victim has suffered extensive damage and what the surgeon aims at is not so much the creation of new features as the restoration of the old as far as he can. Often, alas! full success is impossible, but it is one of the greatest solaces of this war that advances in technique have made so much possible, and so many men have been treated in such a way that they can return to civil life without embarrassment.

A recent case of mine concerned a soldier who came to me for a plastic operation on his face, but the cause was not a war injury. He was thirty-three and after distinguished service in various theatres he was looking forward to his early release and a resumption of the business career he had been following before war called on his services. But his pleasurable anticipations were darkened by doubts and anxieties. He had not made so much progress as he had wished before he had joined the Army. On the contrary he considered that he had been definitely unsuccessful; and he had a very accurate idea of the reason. It lay not in any lack of capacity or ability, but in his appearance.

His work was such that it involved a large amount of interviewing, and the value of a good presence in such circumstances does not need to be stressed. Captain Williams had everything as regards his body: he was fairly tall with broad, well-proportioned shoulders. He was fit in every way. His eyes had the look of determination in them which means a lot when people have to be impressed. But the general air of decision that his figure gave was belied by the shape of his chin.

Though there is little truth in the teachings of physiognomy, there are certain preconceptions and prejudices attached to it which are widely accepted. One of them is that a man with a small and receding chin is weak and lacks the power of decision. This is probably true in a very large number of cases, but it is not a universal law. Captain Williams was certainly an exception. He was possessed of high courage and the ability to make decisions and abide by them, as his war record proved. It was, in fact, his success as an officer during various operations that led him to come and see me. He saw clearly the handicap under which he suffered, and he was determined to have it put right, if that was humanly possible. That alone showed a firmness of an unusual kind.

Certainly his jaw was abnormally small, perhaps half that of the normal man's. Not only so but it receded so sharply that there was barely any ramus at all. The shrewd, steady eyes and the firm mouth could do nothing to offset this drawback. The first thing one noticed about Captain Williams was his chin—or, rather, the absence of it. It was so surprising that one felt oneself saying to oneself: "Is it possible that this is the man who got a commission for bravery in the field and later won rapid promotion for the same reason?"

It was, then, not surprising that he was dreading his return to civil life. He had been relatively inexperienced before the war and perhaps doubted whether he had quite the competence to attain the success he sought. His war experience had resolved all those doubts and shown him clearly where the fault lay.

He told me quite candidly, when he came to see me, that he had had an anxious struggle with himself before he could make up his mind to explore the possibilities of plastic correction. The old prejudice against plastic operations for the mere sake of appearance—as people say slightingly, as though looks mattered nothing and had not practical value—dies hard, especially among men. But he had come to look on his case as desperate. It was; but not quite in the way he thought. It was obvious to me that if he had tried to resume his work in his present state he would be heading for very serious psychological trouble. He would get the impression of being constantly thwarted and frustrated, and the reaction would be all the more severe because of his now absolute confidence in his own abilities—a confidence that was clearly well founded and not just an overweening egotism.

Yet it was difficult to advise him what to do. I told him so.

"I don't care what it is," he said firmly but quietly. "But something must be done."

I considered the case a little and then asked him to come and see me again.

"I have thought it over very carefully," I said, "and what I want to ask you is whether you would be prepared to undergo an operation."

"Of course," he said. "I took it that that would be what you would advise. I should insist upon it."

His decided manner again brought to my mind the contrast between his character and the appearance of his jaw. How easily it was to be misled by prejudices!

"But I want you to understand that the only possible means of doing anything for you is not by a simple plastic operation, like the excision of a small scar or even lifting a face. It is a very serious thing indeed. The only hope I can see is that you have your whole jaw rebuilt by building up the defective parts."

"That still does not alter my mind. I am not afraid of anything like that. The only thing I do fear is having to go through life with this rabbit's chin."

"It is a very drastic procedure and very far from being without risk," I warned him again.

"That makes no difference at all. The risk, whatever it is, is worth while to me. If the operation you propose is the only way, then it must be done."

"Very well," I said. "If I seem over-cautious, it is because I wish you fully to understand the risks."

"I appreciate that, doctor," he replied. "But you can disabuse your mind of the idea that risks of that kind matter to me." He smiled grimly. "I've had some good close-ups of death in the past few years, and this chin has worried me so much that quite often I've wished it had been my turn instead of the other bloke's. So you needn't worry about me even if I don't survive. Quite frankly, I'd rather die, I think, than pull through only to find the whole thing a failure. If you think there is a reasonable chance of success, then carry on."

"I understand." I did. I have come across that attitude in so many different forms in connexion with deformities and abnormalities that it never surprises me. In fact, it is one of the things—and the most important—that reconciles me to Frued's idea of the death wish inherent in all human beings, though at one time I was inclined to ridicule it.

I told him I should like to think a little more before making the final arrangements, as there were certain technical questions to consider. Meanwhile, we could have him photographed, so that I could decide on the exact extent of the reconstruction.

The technique involved in an operation of this kind is lengthy and tricky. It has to be taken in several stages, each one of which introduces an element of risk and uncertainty. Above all it is very tiring and tedious to the patient, who often begins to despair of seeing any tangible results at all. But Captain Williams professed himself ready to put up with anything from acute pain to boredom. I told him that sheer boredom was the most likely thing he would have to endure.

The first stage consists in taking out a special portion of the pelvic bone. Now the pelvis—the hip girdle—is one of the most important supporting structures in the body, and the greatest care has to be taken to ensure that it is not weakened. When this bone has been obtained, the next step is to cut it up into a quantity of minute chips. It is these chips which are inserted into the jaw to build it up and give it shape.

Their introduction is a matter of some difficulty. The rule in all plastic operations is to avoid visible scars, and in any event to make the scars as few as possible. For this reason the tip of the chin has to be reached through an incision made on the inside of the lower lip. While this ensures that there is no scar on the visible parts of the face, it is by no means an ideal position for the subsequent manipulation, since the approach is not as direct as it might be. However, with practice, it is not quite so complicated as it sounds.

Through this incision then, the bone chips are introduced, and they are carefully manipulated into the space in the chin so that they build out the tissues and help them to attain the desired contour. This is the part of the process that is extremely tedious. The surgeon is concerned with minute adjustments which demand a lot of time; but the procedure cannot be hurried, for the patient would certainly not be in a grateful frame of mind if he was presented with a chin which, although no longer receding, suggested some of the wilder excesses of portraiture by a modernist painter.

For this particular case, special bandages had to be devised to hold the chips together until such time as they coalesced and the reconstructed jaw attained stability. This is something which occupies a few weeks, during which the patient suffers all the discomforts of not being able to move his jaw freely.

In every way Captain Williams was an ideal patient. He took quite an interest in what was going on, often making a mild joke about the various proceedings, and he never grumbled or expressed disappointment at what must have seemed to him the monotonous slowness of the work. On the contrary he was buoyed up by the thought that all this was going to mean new life for him, and that a few days or weeks spent under these unpleasant conditions were far better than a life of misery and frustration and failure. He could see the end beyond the means and kept his eyes steadily fixed on it. That was one more tribute to the steadfastness and decision of this character.

He was standing in his room with his back towards the door on the final occasion on which I visited him in hospital. Certainly, I thought, those broad shoulders have an air of purpose. He is an extremely well-built man. As if in commentary on my thoughts, he suddenly turned towards me with a smile. This time, there was no shock at seeing the face. The new jaw matched the body perfectly. He looked what he was: a man of energy, ambition, and decision.

I saw him several times after that, and each time I noticed an improvement in him. Though before there had been no doubt his natural firmness, there had been a suggestion—luckily it had become no more—of a certain shyness and unwillingness to face the world. Gradually all that, the first ominous signs of inferiority feeling, disappeared. His character became more and more openly forceful and compelling. One had the feeling that here was a man who would face anything with the greatest goodwill in the world, and that he was not afraid of anything that might happen to him.

Not very long after the operation, for which he had leave, he received his discharge papers. He had already seen his previous employers, who had of course offered him his old job back. But now he did not consider this was good enough for him. He had no wish to return to a mere junior position, whatever the opportunities might be; and he spent a week or two in interviewing other organizations and companies that might be able to use his services. The upshot was that he was offered, and accepted, a position at more than a thousand a year, with the prospects of earning considerably more in a short while as affairs became more normal.

It was some time later that I learnt of this happy development. He had telephoned me and said he wanted to see me rather urgently. I was alarmed, wondering if something had at long last gone wrong. There was no reason why it should have, but in medicine one is always ready for the unpredictable, I asked him what the trouble was.

"I'll tell you when I see you," he said; and I thought I detected a note of grimness in his voice as he agreed to the time of appointment I suggested.

He came into my room with an almost aggressive air. I glanced at his jaw. Outwardly at least there was nothing wrong with that. He eyed me with a quizzical smile.

"First of all, I've come to thank you, doctor," he began. "It's wonderful what a jaw will do." It was then he told me about his new position; I congratulated him.

"Yes," he went on. "It's quite a good show. But what amuses me is that I saw those people while I was on leave, just before the operation, because I've always had my eye on them, and applied for a job much smaller than this,

They turned me down flat. I hadn't the experience—they didn't think I'd fit in. You know: all the usual excuses. This time, *I* did all the talking. It's amusing."

"Appearances do count for a lot," I commented colourlessly. Was it just for this he had come to see me?

"The credit for my appearance is due to you," he said, "and I'm more than grateful. It's something to think you've had your face made to order and not simply had to put up with what was handed out."

He eyed me again in that odd quizzical way.

"But it doesn't always work out quite so fortunately," he continued reflectively. "That's what I came to tell you about."

Ah! I thought, there's something not quite right after all. All so far has only been the sugar on the pill.

"Is something the matter, then?" I asked.

He laughed joyously. "Oh, no. Nothing's wrong with the job. It's grand. No, it's just an incident that, having got to know you pretty well, I think you'll appreciate. It's a tribute to you, too, in a way, for the complete success of the job."

"What is it then?" I asked.

"I went to see my people. My father's been dead for some years, and my mother and only sister live together in a small cottage in the country down Newbury way. Lovely little place they've got. Ideal for a holiday, though I confess I wouldn't like to live there all the year round. The war has taught me to appreciate such simple pleasures as constant hot water, inside sanitation, and electric light, you see."

"Quite naturally." I had an important appointment almost due, and I was growing a little tired of this obliqueness.

"But I'll get to the point," he said, almost as though I had spoken my thoughts aloud. "I can see I'm wasting your time and you're wishing me to hell. I never thought of anything, of course, and I just went down in the usual way without even telling them I was on the way. I've been down there quite a lot and they know me pretty well in the village, and it struck me as a little peculiar, when I spoke to a chap, that he looked at me with a puzzled air and said "good afternoon" as country people will; but didn't show any signs of recognition. I let it pass out of my mind. Countrymen are curious folk anyhow. You can never be quite sure what they're going to do, even when you live amongst them. I believe my people are still foreigners to the village."

"So your point is that I've given you an inpenetrable disguise?" I asked.

"Well, yes, in a way. But I haven't got to the real point yet. I went up to the cottage and found the door open, as usual, so I just walked in. There was nobody about and I called, but there was no answer, so I concluded they'd slipped out somewhere, and I just dumped myself in an armchair. It was just after the operation, and I admit that at times I was inclined to feel a bit tired.

"After a little while, I heard footsteps and then someone came into the room. I got to my feet and saw Daphne, my sister.

"Of course I grinned. Daph and I have been the closest of pals for years. "Hullo, Daph," I said, and went towards her and tried to kiss her. She sprang back and slapped my face. I was too dumbfounded to do or say anything. "Who are you and what do you want?" she asked, and I was expecting to be pitched out at any moment. Daphne's a tough girl and quite capable of it. Then I realized what it was. She didn't recognize me with my nice new he-man jaw. When that dawned on me, I flopped back in the chair and laughed till I was helpless.

"Even then she took some persuading I was her brother. She thought I was someone trying it on and pretending to be me, and doing it very successfully at that, but for the fact that my make-up was all wrong. But at last I convinced her by showing her the three moles on the back of my neck that she used to make fun of when we were kids together. Then she called Mother in, and told her the joke, and we all had a good laugh together. They're frightfully bucked about it, and think, as I do, you've done a marvellous job."

"I'm glad they're pleased," I said. I was glad, too, that this rather drawn-out account of a very simple and understandable affair was over. I rose from my desk. "And I hope your story of success keeps going," I added, holding out my hand.

"Thank you. Which reminds me—I seem to be doing well all around. There's a girl I know who even thinks my face is "sweet" now. Sweet! With a jaw like this. But I forgive her. You see, I'm going to marry her soon, and then I shall tell her it was you who gave me my lovely square jaw. I know: come to the wedding and I'll make a public announcement of it."

"Thanks," I said, edging him gently towards the door. He was much too talkative. I could understand now his success as an interviewer. "But a doctor never makes appointments long in advance. It's the worst mistake he can make."

"Oh, it won't be as long as that," he said, preparing to leave at last. "I'll see you have a card."

He was gone, and I sank back into my chair with relief. It seemed to me I had given him a new jaw, and at the same time endowed him with the power to wag it.

XVI

NEW FINGERS

To a man who has fought in war, a scar is a badge of honour, a missing limb or digit something of which he may be proud. But though in this last war women have done practically everything except go into the line and fire rifles—they have done even that in Russia and among the various partisans forces—the same attitude of honourable scars has not been applied to them. Hundreds—no, thousands—of women have been injured and wounded, either in doing their jobs with the various Services or as a result of air raids. But the fact that disfigurement was gained in the cause of national defence is often ignored. Above all, it seems, women must be decorative. If they are not decorative, their use is small.

The plastic surgeon learns these things more clearly than the man-in-the-street, because all manner of tales of distress are brought to him. Loss of looks or of figure is a real distress to a woman, and it makes no difference to her whether the disfigurement is due to war causes or the curse of heredity. It may be all right while the girl still wears her khaki or blue; but the moment she again treads the stones of Civvy Street, wounds are wounds, and the best thing that can be done with them is to cover them decently out of the way—which is not so easy in these days of sun-suits.

To many women, disfigurement, however slight, is primarily a psychological burden, often with profound consequences, though not immediately affecting their livelihood. But in some cases abnormality may mean that the shadow of unemployment looms up, and the whole world seems out of joint. In such cases, the plastic surgeon has a great chance to set things right.

It was so with Joan. I had known her slightly before the war when she was a well-known mannequin—though she called herself a "model"—in a fashionable West-End dress house. Then, she had every promise held out to her of rising to the top of her profession. Her name was already known widely, and she was receiving an increasing number of requests from leading photographers to sit as a model for them. It was not merely that she was tall and as slim as a willow, whose grace she seemed to have captured. She had brains as well—real brains. She took an intelligent interest in her work. Her employers often remarked that a gown was nearly as good as sold if Joan modelled it. She was something more than an automaton for the parade of clothes; she employed her wits to present them in the finest possible way.

I once went to a display in which she was taking part, and it struck me then that she avoided all those set poses which have become sheer mannerisms in mannequin's work. Each dress she wore she presented in an entirely different manner, and so immediately attracted attention to it.

Yet for all this success in a profession on which the light of undesirable publicity tends to beat much too brilliantly, she was quiet, unaffected, almost shy, away from her work. She had none of the characteristics of those women whom the court reporters refer to as "mannequins or actresses" when some unsavoury case is heard.

At the beginning of the war, she gave up her job and joined the A.T.S. Many of her friends called her a fool, but she felt that that was what she ought to do, and she did it. The fact of war made the artificiality of the dress world very apparent to her, and she felt suddenly uncomfortable in surroundings where, up till then, she had been very happy. In the much more arduous conditions of the A.T.S., she soon settled down, accepting hardships with cheery goodwill and setting out to do her job as well as she knew how.

There were hardships enough for her during the Blitz, during the whole of which she was stationed in London.

She was bombed out twice from her billets, and once the actual camp where she was working was the target of a special attack in which there were many military casualties. But this did not deter her. It was all in the day's work, and these experiences merely convinced her a little more strongly that she must do all she could. When, therefore, the mixed A.A. batteries were formed, she was glad to find that she had transferred to one of them on actual operational duties. It would give her a chance of getting a little of her own back on the Hun who had already killed and maimed some of her friends.

That opportunity, however, seemed denied to her. The periods of quiet ensued, except for the baby blitzes, as they were called; and life seemed to be all training and routine, without any excitement to relieve it. But if then those who manned the batteries felt bored, they did not know what was in store for them. In June 1944 the flying-bombs began; and for the next three months Joan was to have all the excitement she could have ever desired.

Those were strenuous times for the whole of the Anti-Aircraft Command, and the girls of the A.T.S. did a man's job alongside the men with the greatest honour and distinction. The battery to which Joan was posted alone accounted for fifty of the attackers, and ranked high among all batteries on the south-eastern counties.

In August, just before the major attacks by V1 ceased, a flying-bomb came down almost on the gun-site on which Joan worked. Some of the girls were severely injured, though there were no fatal casualties; and she thought herself lucky at the time to escape with a small fragment of the bomb embedded in her left hand. She reported it at once, though it did not seem very important to her, and she received instant and expert attention.

There, the affair should have ended, but for the unpredictable which dogs all medical work. Infection set in and she was removed to hospital, where she remained for a long time under specialist treatment. The hand grew worse, until at last the surgeon in charge of the case despaired of saving it. But he made a great fight, and in the end, the hand was saved, though the middle finger had to be amputated. After all her service, the price Joan paid for her war experiences was a finger.

No one likes losing a part of his anatomy, especially when it is in so prominent a position as a middle finger, and Joan had a great deal to say on the matter. But she learnt to get along without it, and eventually accepted the position as it was, with the comment that it might have been much worse. Like so many people—of whom I am one—she had always feared being maimed for life even more than death itself.

After a short convalescence, she was passed as fit for service again, though in a lower category, and rejoined her old unit. She was glad to be back with it. It was not one of the batteries that were sent to Belgium, and times grew slack. V2 rockets came over, but they were no concern of A.A. batteries. Preparation for Victory Day mounted, and most of them expected soon to be in action again, as all believed that the Nazis would have one last grand fling at this country which, in 1940, had stood firm against all their attempts at world domination. But the great blitz did not materialize.

Immediately after VE-Day, Joan applied for release. She had had enough and, as she had been wounded, her application on compassionate grounds was accepted. She went straight to her old employers, who welcomed her with open arms. Good mannequins—and she was one of the best—had been scarce during the war. It was a great thing, they thought, to have a first-class one back so soon.

It was true that there was no prospect of an immediate revival in the dress trade so far as the home market was concerned, but the designers were being encouraged to produce clothes for the export trade, and a number of important displays were being planned. Joan's application for re-employment came along exactly at the right moment.

The A.T.S. had done nothing to destroy her figure, as it does that of so many girls. She was still as pretty and as slim as ever. But almost from her first day, she showed signs of not being the same mannequin. All her modelling before the war had been marked by ease, grace, and naturalness, but now there was an air of awkwardness about her that could not be denied. But her employers were considerate. She had been away from it all for a very long time, they told each other, and she might take some time to pick up the threads again. In present conditions especially, she was far too good a model to part with unnecessarily or hastily.

But the expected improvement did not come. On the contrary, she grew worse at each successive appearance. Not only was she shy and reluctant to appear before a number of people, but she could no longer turn freely and naturally. She tried always to conceal her left hand, with the result that her movements became jerky and inartistic.

This was certainly not the type of mannequin that particular house wanted. The managing director took Joan aside and talked to her, and the poor girl nearly burst into tears. She had lost all that self-control and confidence which had previously been so marked in her and contributed to her success.

"I know," she sobbed. "I'm hopeless. But I'm so afraid they may see this awful left hand of mine."

"No one notices it," said the managing director. "And if anyone should chance to, everyone knows how you got it. It's nothing to be ashamed of. You must try not to be so sensitive."

Then and there she wanted to resign, but the managing director would not hear of it. She had only to take herself in hand, he told her. But she had already tried all she knew and failed. There was only one possible outcome, so far as she could see. The end of her career as a mannequin could not be long delayed, and then how could she earn a living? She was too self-conscious of an inferiority to others now to take up modelling for artists and photographers, where the disfigured hand would not matter so much. Clerical work was quite distasteful to her and she had no aptitude for it. The future began to look black, and she wished she had stayed in the A.T.S., even to the extent of signing on for further service, irrespective of demobilization arrangements.

She made all manner of inquiries to find out if anything could be done for her, but there seemed no way out, until a friend of hers suggested, as a last resort, that she should see a plastic surgeon. By some route of which I never obtained complete details, she arrived at my consulting-room.

I listened to her story, with all its familiar details of shyness and inferiority in the presence of others, with growing depression. There was nothing that could be done. One cannot conjure a new finger out of nowhere. But she pressed me hard, and at last, after some consideration, I decided to put to her the proposal of building a new finger.

Immediately I mooted the idea her eyes brightened. Here was the ray of hope for which she had so long sought in vain. But I quickly set about showing her that it was by no means simple, and that even if it was successful, she would not be able to use the finger much, as it would have no middle joint. She would be in exactly the same position as the person with an ankylosed joint.

"I don't mind that," she said. "It would be better—ever so much better—than no finger at all. At least it would look natural."

"Oh yes," I said, "it would be perfectly normal in appearance, and especially when it was gloved no-one would suspect what had been done. But it isn't a simple operation, and it's necessary for you to understand it fully, for I shall want your consent to making certain experiments."

"I'll consent to anything," she replied. "The only thing that matters is whether there's a chance of pulling it off."

"I think there is."

At some length, and in greater detail than is usual on these occasions, I told her what I proposed to do. Despite her protestations that she was ready for anything, her face grew grave as I proceeded, and I fully expected to find she had changed her mind when I had finished. But then she smiled.

"You've been making my spine wiggle," she said. "I hate talking about operations. But that's O.K. I'm quite ready for you to do anything you want to do."

So the operation was put in hand—or rather series of operations. First of all, I obtained close measurements of her existing middle finger on the right hand, and compared these with the general dimensions of her left. Her two hands appeared to be symmetrical, which made my task a little, if not much, easier. Then the operations proper began. By way of introduction, an incision was made over her ribs and three small pieces of bone, the size of a single phalanx of her existing middle finger, were excised. Next a fold of skin was cut from her abdomen, and the three pieces of bone were enclosed within it. This skin was not removed altogether, but an attachment was left at one end, so that the flap could be rolled over the bone pieces to enclose them in a tube, which was then sealed by stitches all round the free edges.

This concluded the first stage of the procedure, and Joan was sent to bed to let the manufactured finger heal. It took about three weeks before it was completely healed, and now I began the second stage.

The old scar that covered the place where the missing finger had been was carefully excised and a fresh wound was made. Then the left hand was brought to the new "finger", where it lay attached to the abdomen. The latter had also been opened up at the nearer end, and the two fresh wounds were brought together and stitched into position.

Once again, Joan was forced to live a life of inactivity, very much against her inclinations, for some three weeks. By that time, complete union had been effected. All the while she had had her left hand bound to her abdomen—an experience that is, to any normal person, a little trying, to say the least, but she bore it all with good humour, and said she wished she could use it because she wanted to scratch. The joke was weak, but it revealed her spirit, and also the hopeful outlook she maintained towards it all, a very encouraging sign.

In the third stage, the bridge of skin holding the finger to the abdomen was severed so as to free the hand, in which the new finger was now in place. After another period of rest, the job was declared finished.

I do not think I shall ever forget the first time she looked at her hand after the treatment was concluded. For an appreciable time she stared at it silently, as though quite unable to believe her eyes. Then slowly she looked at me and there were tears glistening on her eyelashes.

"It's wonderful," she said in a subdued voice, that was at the same time throbbing with delight. "It's as if a miracle had happened." And again she stared at the finger, wondering perhaps when this fantastic dream would fade.

Once again I warned her that she would not be able to move the finger, except from the base, but that did not seem to worry her in the slightest. That horrid, accusing gap had disappeared. She no longer felt that everyone was staring at her and making comments, perhaps pitying her and saying: "What a pity! And she's such a good-looking girl, too."

She came back a little while afterwards for examination, and she and I agreed that the new finger was a little out of shape as compared with the other fingers and with those of the right hand. This was something which could be remedied, though I believe she would have been quite content if things had been left as they were.

A special mould, based on the shape of the other fingers, was made and the two halves were hinged down one side, very like the little cases in which cigarette holders are contained. Every night she placed the finger in this mould, which shaped the digit as required. At the end of a short period, the finger assumed a more normal shape, until it was only on the closest inspection that its "artificiality" could be determined.

Relieved now and feeling perfectly confident again, she

went back to her old employers, who had given her special leave all this time, and told them she felt thoroughly fit for work again. From what she subsequently told me, I believe they were as delighted as she was, for they were loath to part with a girl who, apart from this one blemish, was so outstanding in her work. It was three months later when she called on me and told me the house was again giving her all its most important modelling work to do.

I examined the finger as a matter of course. There was nothing at all the matter with it, and I felt very pleased with my work. But that was not my chief source of self-congratulation. As always it was the psychological change that had affected me most. She had come to me originally depressed, worried, almost despairing. I saw her now when she was gay and self-confident, happy in the work she loved. Once again, I felt, plastic surgery had been the means of reintegrating a personality and restoring what the surgeon's knife by itself can now replace: the full joy of living as a normal human being.

XVII

A JOURNEY THROUGH THE SKULL

Perhaps the greatest gift of war is that the whole of a nation's available resources are turned to the discovery of new and better treatments. The pity is that the same thing cannot be done in peace. The result is that progress in medicine generally is extremely rapid, and a case incurable one year may be brought into the curable class before twelve more months have passed. It is as though man, having let loose death upon the world, strengthens his defences against death and suffering itself. Man is, indeed, a curious animal, and will never attain the perfection of which he is capable until he has learnt to master the savage instincts which still linger in him.

This war has brought many new boons to medicine. A large number of new surgical techniques have been developed—techniques which, designed to save precious manpower in the years of death, will continue to bring in increasing measure rich harvests in times of peace. The Truetta method of dealing with wounds is alone a significant advance. No less important have been the new drugs made available together with the development of older ones. The sulphonamide series has been known for some time, but it has been war that has won for it universal recognition, while the story of penicillin has often been told.

Perhaps too much has been written about penicillin, and it has had a little more than its fair share of popularization. The result is that it has been hailed virtually as the ever-elusive panacea, and even doctors have been led on to ask more of it than it can perform. Like everything else it has its own field of usefulness and its own limitations. But that field of usefulness is so large, and the crops cut in it are so fine, that they need no exaggeration.

In my work, I have often found penicillin of the most remarkable help, and there are many cases in which I have used it that are worthy of relating. But here one only is needed; and it is in some ways the most extraordinary of its kind with which I have been concerned.

James Tebbutt—Jim to all his friends—was the manager of a large firm engaged in optical-instrument manufacture. He knew his job thoroughly and loved it, and he went about life with a fine zest. At sixty, he was as happy as any man could be, asking nothing better than to spend his leisure with his four children, and his beloved wife. But the time for such family reunions had passed with the war, though he was looking forward to their resumption as soon as peace should come. He himself worked long hours, and when the factory did not claim him he devoted himself wholeheartedly to Civil Defence, since he was District Warden in his borough and took his unpaid services very seriously indeed. Two of his sons were in the Forces and abroad. It was a family that was pulling its full weight in the war effort.

During the blitz someone christened him Lucky Jim. Certainly he seemed to bear a charmed life. Despite his hard work during the day, he was out every night, and his area had more than its fair share of incidents. But even when a high-explosive bomb came down within fifty yards of him, he escaped without a scratch, and once he had just emerged from searching a badly damaged building when it collapsed to the ground in a pile of rubble. He did not mind telling his stories of those hectic days when London was the front line, but it was always with a keen eye for the funny side and an almost indecent modesty which suggested that really he had been no more than a curious onlooker who had got in the way of the services.

The lull came and he was glad of it. Things began to look more hopeful overseas, first with the victories in Africa and Italy, and then with the landing in Normandy. The blitz he expected as an accompaniment of D-Day did not materialize, and he allowed himself to look forward to the return of his two sons and a long and much-needed holiday with his whole reunited family by the sea. The world looked good to him.

Then came the flying-bombs and Civil Defence, with much depleted ranks (for its full-time workers had been seriously reduced) was put to the full stretch for three weary months. Once again people called him Lucky Jim. Nothing could touch him. When others in his own factory became casualities during a daylight incident, Jim was unscathed and took charge of the proceedings.

With the end of these attacks, and the progress in France and Belgium, he did really feel that the end was in sight. It was very nearly—but not in the sense in which he meant. Lucky Jim had had a good run for his money, and, as so often happens, his luck was to break at the last moment.

After the flying bombs, the V2s came. The incidents, though few, were serious, but his luck still held—till the very end. Almost the last rocket to descend on this country struck his borough. More than that, it hit his district at a moment when he was taking a look round the various wardens' posts. A fragment of flying debris hit him on the back of the head, causing extensive surface injuries and at the same time, and more seriously, fracturing his skull. His luck had gone with a vengeance. It was as though this had been carefully saved up for him.

That was how I first met Lucky Jim. He was brought into the hospital while I was on E.M.S. duty, and we set to work at once. A few pieces of stone were extracted from the wounds and the fracture of the skull was set. The rest very largely depended upon him. He was not too young—we could see that, but we also knew that he was a man of irrepressible vigour who believed in life and the fullness thereof. Taking everything into consideration, we decided that the chances were not unfavourable. His luck might have turned on him, but perhaps now it would come back in renewed strength.

That, in fact, is what seemed to be happening. For two weeks he made excellent progress, and everyone concerned with the case was highly satisfied. There were no complications. Healing was taking place normally, and the bones in the broken skull were reuniting. Then the whole picture changed almost instantaneously.

His temperature chart, which till then had showed a reassuring evenness, suddenly shot up into a sharp peak, and he complained of violent headaches. These were dangerous signs and symptoms. They could mean only that infection had sent in; and when infection sets in in such cases, the prognosis is grave. We did what we could, but it did not help, and I was not at all surprised when an X-ray photograph revealed an abscess on the brain.

This looked like the very end of Jim's luck. His turn had come at last. But it was not 1940. If Jim had come to us then and gone through the same stages, he would have been regarded as a sure fatality. Patients with abscesses on the brain simply did not live. But it was 1944, and there was penicillin available. If it could be introduced, it might secure the right result—the break-up of the abscess. But the problem lay in that "if". The brain is sealed off from the outside world by a thick bowl of bone; moreover it actively resents most attempts at interference with it.

Still, penicillin was the one chance; and that chance had to be taken if Jim's life was not to be allowed to slip away without a fight. I discussed the matter with the other surgeons, and we agreed that there was one thing worth trying. We could bore two holes in his skull, insert a special type of metal tube, and then go gently forward till the tube reached the cavity containing the pus. In this way we could introduce the life-giving drug to the place where it could do its work. The object of the two holes was to provide ducts whereby the prurient matter could be drained away. This had to be done first, and not till then was the penicillin, in solution, injected.

It was not at all a pleasant operation to perform, but it had to be done. The case was growing more urgent almost every minute. We set to work and eventually we were able to draw off the decaying matter. Then we gave the first administration of penicillin. That was all for the time being. But three hours later, the whole procedure of drainage and injection was repeated again; and so it went on every third hour for two full days.

During those trying forty-eight hours, it was touch-and-go with Jim. Balancing up the probabilities it did not seem likely that he could or would live. But always when he seemed on the point of going, he managed to rally somehow, and there was never any need to discontinue the regular sequence of treatment. Perhaps, after all, his luck had not deserted him as we thought it had.

And then, with a suddenness almost like that with which the infection had originally developed, he took a turn for the better. By the time we discontinued treatment the issue was no longer in doubt. Most decidedly, Jim's luck was still with him, though there were still some fences to be taken, and it is always unwise to count one's chickens before they are hatched in the medical poultry-yard. I was quite prepared at any time to hear that he had collapsed suddenly; and if he did that, our resources could provide nothing further for him. We had gambled our last coin and could make no more stakes.

None of my forebodings was fulfilled. The case made excellent progress, and each time I saw Jim he seemed a little more his normal self. There had been, quite expectedly, indications of facial paralysis when the infection had got a hold; these now began to disappear. He complained less and less of headaches, and was well enough to remark that it was a good job he was in hospital as he would never have been able to afford all the aspirins he would have taken for that head. That was the most encouraging sign of all: the gradual return of his old spirits. Jim had never evaded danger, however much it seemed to have avoided him. But he was not one of those who would give up life without a struggle. He had, he said, all a man needed for complete happiness in this world: a perfect wife, good children, and a first-class job.

"Take all your riches and dump them into the sea," he said to me once. "I don't want 'em. What good do they do you? As long as you've a good missis and decent kids, a good home to go home to, and enough put by not to have to worry about the future or the turn of bad luck—what more do you want?"

I could not answer this simple, sturdy creed of life.

It was two weeks after we began the penicillin treatment that we considered him fit enough to be discharged from the hospital. But we did not consider him cured. What he needed now was a good rest amid pleasant surroundings. I advised him to take a long convalescence, stressing the fact that though he was a remarkably fit man for his age, there were penalties of years we could not escape.

He nodded. "I know. I'm wonderfully fit, thank God," he said, "but I know my limitations. They grow on you as the years go by so that you don't notice till you try to pull out the little extra you used to be able to and find you can't do it. It's this incurable disease I'm suffering from."

I could see he was indulging in one of his little jokes, but I pretended to be puzzled.

"I'm afraid my examination didn't reveal that," I said.

"And you call yourself a doctor, and you can't recognize it? Well, well. *Anno domini*, doctor. You'll never cure that, penicillin or no penicillin."

I sent him away with that and told him to come and see me as soon as he felt completely restored, adding that he was on no account to hurry things. I knew he liked his annual holiday, but I knew also that he loved his work and was anxious to get back to it, and that no place, however pleasant in itself, could ever be a substitute for the little house which had been his home for over thirty years.

I had almost forgotten about the case when I saw the name Tebbutt entered in my appointment book, and I had to pause for a moment to recollect who this might be. Then I remembered. Lucky Jim, of course. I wondered whether he still considered himself lucky.

The next afternoon he came in breezily. There was no doubt of his complete recovery. He was as spry as any man of his age could be. To my surprise he was wearing his warden's uniform, with the three yellow bars on the upper sleeve by the shoulder denoting his rank. He saw me glance at it.

"Yes, I'm fond of the old uniform," he said, "though a lot of people seem to despise it. Besides, look at that." He turned his left arm and showed me a single gold vertical stripe. "Happened just in time for me to get my wound stripe," he pointed out proudly.

I smiled to myself. He had the enthusiasm of a child.

"Yes, my luck held, even when they thought it had left me," he said as though answering the question that had been in my mind when I had seen his name.

"So you still consider yourself lucky?" I asked.

"Why not? I've had all the luck. If what you say is right, doctor, then if I'd got that packet during the blitz you wouldn't have had any of that penicillin stuff to do the trick, and it would have been lights out for me. That correct, isn't it?"

"Yes. You were lucky there."

"Then I've had a glorious time down in the country, and I come home just in time to hear both my boys are due in England in the same week. More luck, you see."

I was pleased by his easy optimism.

"Do you consider it lucky to have a couple of holes in your head?" I asked. There were still two depressions in his skull where we had made the holes. They were covered by soft tissue, but the bone beneath is missing, and they are soft under pressure.

He looked at me as though I was little mad.

"Why, that's the luckiest thing of the lot," he said with complete conviction. "Don't you see it's given me the best story any man ever had in years? I can ask my friends to feel where the doctors went in to make a journey through my skull. You should see their faces when I tell them that. You wouldn't think it unlucky if you could."

"I'm glad you take it that way. Other people might not be so pleased about it," I remarked.

"There are too many people who can see only the black side of things," he commented firmly. And then he grew serious. "There's one other thing I was lucky about—and that was real luck," he said earnestly. "I was taken to the right hospital. I'm sure if I'd been sent to some hospitals, they'd never have pulled me round."

"Don't be silly. We only did what any competent surgeon would have done," I returned.

"Maybe. But competent surgeons aren't so common, if you ask me." He rose and held out his hand. "I'm really grateful to you, doctor, and all this talk about luck is just my fun. You saved my life, and if I was so patched up I could only just walk, I'd still be grateful. You can't pay too high a price for life, you know."

That summed up his philosophy. Perhaps it is a good one. I do not know. But in his own case he is certainly right.

XVIII

THIS NOBLE SPIRIT

There lies before me a letter from a very dear friend. Though it was written two years ago it moves me deeply still, for it is the most splendid expression of friendship and gratitude that has ever been written. I say that deliberately. It stirs me, too, because of the memories it evokes, above all the memory of a great and noble woman who showed patience and courage under the greatest suffering, and whose thoughts turned ever outwards from herself to consider those who, she knew, were suffering with her and for her.

Many letters of gratitude reach me at various times. A few are formal, some patently insincere; the majority thank me for a life saved, for something restored. This letter which is open now on my desk is like none of those others. It is a salute to a noble spirit on its passing, and the salute extends to me the hand of friendship. Here are none of the vain regrets, the hackneyed phrases, of those whose feelings do not lie deep; there is the simple dignity of grief felt in the very core of the soul, that which can rise above the agony of the moment and touch the stillness of the stars.

This is not the place to print that letter, which was intended for my eyes alone, and which shall remain forever secret as among my most treasured possessions, something of which only I can appreciate the full flavour. But the associations will be the better for the telling, my own valediction to that same spirit of whom the letter writes . . .

It began in 1941. I was called to the flat of my friend to see his mother. His manner was grave. For some time his mother had suffered from very severe pains, which she had sought to minimize, but now they could no longer be denied. He thought it was very serious.

I knew how fond he was of his mother. Their relationship was an outstanding example of the purest relationship that can exist between man and woman: the mutual adoration of mother and son. There was, he explained, no other life dearer to him in the world. I was to do everything possible.

The mother had been known to me for some time. I had always admired her calm grace and cheerful smile. Though she was now pale and worn and weak, she still retained both to a remarkable degree. I have never known a more serene patient. It was as though she found in pain and suffering some supreme sublimation of spirit, a fire that refined rather than consumed.

As soon as I had made a cursory examination, I feared the worst, though I gave no sign then to either son or mother. This was no mere gastric case. The grim word "cancer" crossed my mind, but for the moment I thought it better to say nothing. I had no desire to shock this son whose solicitude for his mother was so deep and genuine, though I knew that he was prepared to hear the worst.

It was, then, only when I was quite sure in my own mind, that I asked him to call at my consulting rooms, where I told him the truth.

"It is a very serious case, I said. "It is not theoretically inoperable, but I have grave doubts of the wisdom of an operation."

He looked at me sadly but seriously. "That is what I feared," he said. "I have suspected it for some time. But surely there is some chance? We cannot let her of all people go like that, without a fight, the victim of intense agony."

"Frankly, I hardly know what to say," I returned. "It would be a serious enough business in a young and fit person, but your mother is getting on in years, and the long suffering she has endured has lowered her vitality. It is a matter for very serious consideration, yet at the same time it is extremely urgent."

He thought for a moment, his face expressionless. Then he looked at me.

"I think it should be done, George. I am sure she would wish it herself. If it was anyone else but you, I might be doubtful, but she and I trust you implicitly. We know that you will take no undue risks, and that quite apart from professional considerations you will act as the true friend you are."

"That is generous of you, Robin," I replied, "and I do not know how to acknowledge that tribute, which is more than I deserve. But I have a proposal to make in all seriousness. If this operation is performed, I would rather not take the sole responsibility for it. Here, a very precious life is concerned. She is infinitely more dear to you than to me, of course, yet I hold her in the greatest affection and honour."

"What do you propose?" he asked.

"That I call in the greatest specialist in this field and ask him if he will operate with me. It is the best way."

He made a gesture of dissent. "There is no need for that, George," he said. "As I have said, we trust you as we trust no other doctor, whatever his reputation. I understand your feelings, yet I think I would prefer that you did it alone."

I shook my head. The risk was too great. This case demanded the highest skill available. A surgeon must never allow his own pride to stand in the path of the right treatment. I would have been the last to assert that my skill in abdominal operations of this kind was the equal of that of the man whose name was known not merely to the whole of the medical profession in England but also all over the world.

"I must insist," I said decidedly. "It is the only way in which I can consent to undertake the case at all."

"Very well, George, if that is how you feel, it must be that way. But I do want you to understand that we regard this as your choice. We ourselves are quite satisfied to place this precious life, as you called it, in your hands and your hands alone."

"Thank you, Robin," I said. "Your very attitude makes the course I propose all the more necessary. None of us is complete master of his unconscious reactions, and the very fact that I know how much your mother means to you might depress the standard of my work through over-anxiety. I do not say it would, but it is a risk, and there are risks enough in this case without introducing fresh ones."

He agreed and I promised to communicate with the specialist at once and let him know the result.

The great man listened to me, and at first I think he would have turned the case down on the ground that it was hopeless, and the slight chance of success was barely worth taking. But I would not accept this view, much though I sympathized with his feelings, which I had already experienced to some degree. Eventually he consented to get into my car and drive to the flat to make his own examination.

There was a double motive in my forcing this course upon him. In the first place it was, of course, essential that he should see the case and form his own independent judgment. In the second, I felt that Robin's arguments added to my own might induce him to reconsider.

I still think it was Robin's sincerity and simple appeal that won him over, for he was not merely a great authority and a surgeon of outstanding skill, but also a great humanitarian. He was moved by the deep bond of attachment between mother and son. I believe too that the quiet unbreakable courage of the patient herself affected him. Here, indeed, was a woman for whom no effort could be too great.

No surgeon, whether world-famous or not, would allow such personal matters to lead him to an utterly wrong and outrageously risky line of conduct, but where the decision lies balanced on a knife edge they are often the decisive factor. They certainly were here.

The operation was duly made. There was nothing very special about it in the technical sense, though it was an exceedingly bad case of abdominal cancer, and I found it difficult to understand why I had not been called in before. But the explanation was simple, when I came to think of it. This lady would not show she was suffering until the pain overwhelmed her. Even then she would minimize it and try to make it seem less than it was, especially to her son, whose feelings she so closely studied. Practically the whole of the large intestine was affected.

We knew—the specialist and myself—that at most we were doing no more than prolonging a life that was already doomed. Robin, too, knew it. But even a few months more of his mother's company, even the thought that she might be spared a little of the pain—these boons were worth the price.

For two days after the operation she seemed to be making good progress and our slender hopes grew stronger. Her quiet courage and unquenchable spirit were helping her in our fight—not so much because she valued life in itself as because she knew that her life was infinitely precious to others, her husband and her son. But on the third day, our hopes ebbed. Complications ensued, and infection set in.

This would have been the end, but for the resources of the modern chemist. We called in the sulphonamide drugs to our aid. There was some improvement, but it was neither extensive enough nor rapid enough to bring about the desired result in time. The difficulty was to combat the infection while her strength, which was proving greater than we had thought, lasted.

There was one more resource available—penicillin. But supplies then were scarce and reserved almost entirely for the use of the Forces. With great difficulty we managed, however, to secure a supply, and when she was treated with this life-saving miracle, the recovery was complete. It looked as though that faith which moves mountains was coming strongly to our side, for Robin never wavered in his belief that we would pull her through, and in her moments of wakefulness the mother looked at us with eyes that spoke of trustful hope.

It was a long and weary fight, but at long last we were able to send her home. Her gratitude knew no bounds.

And then followed eighteen months of one of the most remarkable experiences of my professional career. She was weak, and only a shadow of her younger self, yet she behaved in a perfectly normal way. One would hardly suspect she was one of the chosen of death, and that all we had done was to postpone the day of her summons. Not one complaint escaped her.

I shall always recall my visits during that time. I called regularly, never daring to make any call my last, for each time I saw her the thought crossed my mind: "This is too good to be true. One day she will have a sudden collapse." And I was ungenerous enough—and unjustified enough, as events showed—to imagine that in such circumstances Robin might accuse me of neglect and complacency. He was the last person in the world I wished to offend or hurt.

There was one day when she looked at me with that quiet smile which lingers yet in my memory. It had a quality of curious peace about it, and it always suggested timelessness to me. Thus, I imagined, she might smile through the centuries, never growing older, never allowing the vicissitudes of life to ruffle her. Old though she was, one could never associate the weaknesses of age with her. She was ageless, eternal.

"George," she said in her weak, yet calm, voice. "You are a very attentive and charming doctor. I value you, too, as a great friend. I think you should receive some recognition of your merits."

"No doctor could fail to be attentive and charming when he had a patient like you," I returned, knowing her liking for the type of compliment that is now considered a thing of the past.

She smiled faintly. "You are also a flatterer, and that deserves no recognition," she remarked. "But quite seriously I should like you to accept a little token of my appreciation for all your care. I know you have always admired those two Sèvres cups in the cabinet there, and I ask you to accept them now with the gratitude of all of us for all your care and attention."

"That is very marvellous of you," I said, "but it is entirely unnecessary and . . ."

But she would hear no protests. Even in her weakness of body, she still had a strength of mind that could not be gainsaid. A little later when I left I bore a parcel which had been very carefully made up by Robin. It contained the two Sèvres cups, which I handled with tenderness. The old lady was quite right: I had always coveted those two fine specimens, but I never thought that they would one day be mine.

In those days, there was an air of peace and harmony in the household that was a joy to experience. The son tended his mother unceasingly, allowing no-one else to look after her unless it was essential. And she watched his every movement with a closeness and affection that moved the beholder. Once or twice I caught her smiling at me enigmatically, as though she and I shared a secret that was not for the others to know. It puzzled me a little, though I believe afterwards I knew what it meant.

She was as calm and peaceful as ever. Yet she would rarely reply direct to my invariable question: Any sign of pain?

Her reply to that was as enigmatic as the smile I intercepted.

"Don't be silly, George. Pain is an illusion. If I said I had pain I should probably be deceiving myself and you. I am quite well."

But though the weeks lengthened into months, and the months into a year, and she still seemed the same, content with her quiet existence in the care of her adored son, I was still not without anxiety. The plain fact was that the end must come. I dreaded each visit, since I expected to be greeted not with the usual smiles but with expressions of grief. And each time my dark foreboding went unfulfilled.

Then one morning she complained of sickness and pain. I was called at once and lost no time in reaching her home. I could see that it was hopeless. The end was near, but even then I could not say how long it might be delayed.

It was two weeks later that she died. I was summoned at one o'clock in the morning to her bedside, at her own express wish. Robin looked pale; he was obviously suffering intensely though he was now prepared for the inevitable. The old lady turned her eyes and smiled. It was no longer an enigmatic smile; it had an air of finality that was almost terrifying. She was accepting the end as quietly and as nobly as she had lived, and even the cold hand of death on hers did not cause her to quail or falter in her supreme serenity.

A little later she died. I left the house to those whose grief was too deep to be shared or witnessed even by one who had been proud to call himself their friend.

As I drove home, I thought of that last smile, one of the bravest things I have ever seen. I thought, too, of those other smiles she had given me, and I believed now I knew what their secret was.

To me, now, looking back on all things, it seems plain that the peace of that household was that peace which precedes the storm and ushers in the tragedy. It was the deliberate creation of that old lady, whose spirit now walked the Elysian fields reserved for those of the highest courage. In those eighteen months, when her calmness had surprised me, she had felt pain, but she had concealed it. She had seen the grief her former collapse had caused, and she would not have that occur again. She knew with her clear foresight that the end must come, and she was resolved that while she was spared she would make the few remaining weeks or months a time of utter happiness and unity with those two whom she loved above all else: her husband and her son.

I know of no greater courage than that—the deliberate suppression of personal feelings of the most acute and agonizing kind for the greater happiness of those around her. I have used the word noble in connexion with her many times, but it is the only way to describe her. In that old lady, nobility reached its apex.

A little while later, that letter reached me. It was an affectionate letter, paying me tributes that I ill deserved. And I could feel the warmth of true friendship emanating from it even through the cold black and white of ink upon paper. It told me, too, of the affection I had inspired in the old lady herself, for it revealed that the two Sèvres cups she had given me had been bequeathed to me by her will, which had been made some time before the operation. That is something I shall always remember. It is perhaps more moving to be remembered as a friend than as a surgeon pure and simple.

I saw Robin himself a little while later. He was still grave, but he made no conventional expressions of his sorrow.

"I can never thank you enough, George," he said.

"But what did I do? Nothing."

"Nothing?" He seemed surprised. "I knew as well as you did that the operation only delayed the end and that death must come. But you lifted the burden of pain from her, you gave her back to us for many months that I will always remember as the most stirring and happy of my life. I think you sensed something of the beauty of those last few months. You have it in you to do such things. And if you think that it is nothing to bring happiness to three people, happiness even in the shadow of death, then you are a strange man indeed."

I shook my head and said no word. For I think he had spoken the only epitaph his mother would have liked to have. She had determined that those months should be graven on their memories as a time of peace. He had called them beautiful. It was the right and fitting word.

XIX

THE SURGEON-ENGINEER

I have often wondered if the public—and for that matter surgeons themselves—realize how much modern surgery owes to the engineer. It is the engineer who has given us the boon of stainless steel and of knives and instruments of a precision and keenness that would have surprised even the previous generation of doctors. It is the engineer who has brought to the operating theatre lighting that enables one to work without shadows, those pitfalls that may trap one to fatal mistakes, and who has devised systems that obviate the danger of black-outs due to current failure. The imposing apparatus of the diagnostician to-day owes very much indeed to the engineer and his close ally the physicist, with its X-ray tubes and cameras, its beautiful lenses, and its meters. It is but another and a striking example of the truth that modern civilization depends upon the engineer, as the ancient ones did on the slave. But whereas the slave-driver harnessed human beings to the needs of the times, the engineer makes the forces of nature do the work.

One may admit all this and still fail to see how the engineer and his wonderful inventions can be of the utmost direct help to the mender of human bodies. Indeed, it is easier to see the engineer's contributions to the science of death, even to the point of wishing that the ingenuity which produces flying bombs and rocket projectiles, jet-driven aeroplanes and magnetic mines had never come to fruition.

During the blitz, there was a case that brought all this very much to the front of my mind, for it was one in which, when the surgeon had done all he could, the engineer stepped in and made possible life for an individual who otherwise would have had little more than a bare existence.

It had been a bad night in the early days of the London raids—a night on which the capital obtained far too much evidence of the devastating effects of parachute mines. One had come down in the early morning and just before three o'clock the casualties began to come in. Among them was a man who was obviously dying. His condition was beyond description, and the wonder was that the spark of life still flickered in that shattered form. In fact, the only indication that he was alive at all was the stertorous breathing from his lungs. The stretcher bearers told me his name was John.

Later I learnt quite a good deal of his tragic history, so let me start at the beginning and lead up to the events which followed.

John was sixty-five, and even his mangled body showed that he had been a fine man physically. For thirty years he had enjoyed the happiest of family lives, and he had discharged for some years past the duties of a foreman in a radio factory. Till the war came no tragedy had clouded his life. He was one of those who found joy in the uneventful routine of work and domestic relaxation, and he asked neither for great pleasures or their complement, great pains.

But the war thrust sorrow into his life as it did into the lives of thousands of others. The first stroke was the loss of his son in the Dunkirk evacuation. That boy had been his chief pride, and a golden future had been planned for him. He had gone by way a scholarship at a secondary school to London University and when the war broke out was in the second year of the electrical-engineering course. He did not wait for "directions" or conscription. He joined the Army two days before the outbreak of War, despite his father's lack of enthusiasm for the idea, and his unit had been one of the reinforcements thrown in in vain attempt to stem the German deluge.

The loss hit John terribly. But he took it in the characteristic English way. He came from the North, and the North does not show its feelings readily. John said little, but it was obvious that something very important had passed from his life. His dourness grew more marked and his sense of discipline increased.

The blitz had come, and John and his family spent every night in the tiny cellar of their little basement, making it as comfortable as they could. They made a joke of it, calling it their rabbit-hole; but the strain was telling on them. And then came the night to which I have already referred. The parachute-mine came down at the corner of the road, and what had once been John's cherished home became a mound of rubble lit by the flames of surrounding fires.

When he was brought to me, he could not have known anything. They could not had they wished have told him of the fresh tragedy that had burst into his ordered life. A daughter of his had been killed outright. His wife and three other children had been dug out of the wreckage; they were terribly bruised and shocked, but they were still alive, and their cases were not desperate, though serious enough. And John . . . well, I have already said something of the condition in which he was brought to the hospital.

I made the examination with a sinking heart while my assistant and the sister made ready for an operation that all of us already considered hopeless. A large piece of casing had torn away part of his neck and the other injuries were too extensive even to be catalogued. I very nearly gave it up then and there, but the motto of "Send them back alive" spurred me on. At least we could try.

We did try. For ten hours we dealt with that mangled body, and at the end of the most exhausting operation I have ever known, we sent out from the theatre a living corpse that was barely human, even in form. He could neither hear not speak, for the upper part of the windpipe and the throat had been completely destroyed by that vicious fragment. There was not much in life for him to look forward to if he survived. The wonder was that he had lived so long. Perhaps it was his Lancashire toughness that pulled him through.

I saw no more of John after that. He was passed into the ward for chronic patients and received regular, routine care, under which he managed in some sort of way to continue to live. It was in fact as long as six months later when, passing through that ward, I recognized him and inquired about his progress.

The nurse shrugged her shoulders.

"He's still alive and doesn't want to be," she said. "The only way of communicating with him is by writing. He can use his hands. That's why he's got that writing pad with the pencil tied on to it."

As if in commentary on this remark, he signed to me to approach and as I drew near to his bed he began scribbling on the pad, which he held up for me to see.

"I'm sorry I ever got through that operation," he had written.

It was not a very good reward for all we had done that night, but I felt inclined to agree with him. He was not thinking of myself. The nurse told me he carried on quite lengthy communications at times with his pad, and he was always thinking of the survivors of his family. In his present state, though he would soon be able to walk about a little he could not go back to his job. It was doubtful if he could go to any job, for a man, deaf, dumb, and horribly scarred, is not the most welcome of employees. And that meant starvation not merely for him but for the others . . . He might get a pension under the Civilian Casualties scheme, but it would barely be enough to keep body and soul together. No doubt he was insured, as most men of his class are, through the weekly collection schemes, and it is one of the ironics of our system that a widow is better off as a rule than a wife with a living but crippled husband.

I felt annoyed—not at his pencilled message to me, for I knew it had reason in it, but at the general hopelessness of the case. There is nothing less satisfactory than saving a life only to find that it is useless.

On my way back to Harley Street, I mused on his case, and suddenly remembered that he had been a foreman in a radio factory. Next time I went to the hospital, I looked up his record and found out the name of the firm. A fantastic idea had entered my head. The surgeon was going to call in the engineer to his aid.

The chief engineer of the firm gladly agreed to see me. He was a cordial man, wrapped up in his work, and I felt from the first that he would lend a sympathetic ear to my proposals, however wild and extravagant they might seem.

"Yes," he said, when I said I had come about John, "it was a real raw deal for him. I liked him very much personally—known him for years. And he was one of our best men. The place isn't the same without him, and we've never quite succeeded in finding a good substitute in his shop."

This was encouraging. If there was a way of helping him back to fitness, these people would do it, in their own interests.

With some hesitation, for I am as ignorant as a child in engineering matters—more ignorant than many modern children—and do not even known what goes on under the bonnet of my car, I outlined my ideas. The chief engineer listened attentively and with mounting interest. At last he became enthusiastic. But it was not, as I expected it would be, because I suggested a chance of restoring to his firm a good workman; it was solely and simply because of the technical problems involved.

He began to talk rapidly in a language I did not understand, addressing his remarks to his chief assistant, who had been with him all the time. They talked of resonance and decibels, of damped vibrations and ohms and watts and amperes. I remember the words, but I still am hazy about their meaning.

I went away certain that if the thing was possible it would be done. It was a month or so later when Mr. Trayle, the engineer, called me on the telephone and asked if I could spare the time to see a piece of apparatus he had built in his experimental shop. I said I could come at once, and he seemed delighted.

When I looked at it I could scarcely believe my eyes and ears. The vague idea I had put to the engineer had developed into a complicated and wonderful instrument. It was a special form of amplifier—I think that is the right word, though I always think of it as a radio apparatus—which has a collar that is attached to the wearer's neck. A special vice makes contact with the upper end of the windpipe, and another is placed in the mouth. When the wearer places the latter in his mouth and whispers, the words he utters are passed through the amplifier and a pleasant, deep-toned voice emerges from the loud speaker.

With all the enthusiasm of a child with a new toy, the engineers demonstrated this new marvel. Indeed, I gained the very distinct impression that they were playing with it, for they produced from it all manner of noises, some strange and some curiously beautiful, that no normal person would want to employ. Then they asked me if I was satisfied or if I thought it was too cumbersome.

I was more than satisfied; I was delighted, and I told them so. It had turned out far better than I had hoped. I had thought dimly of an apparatus that would enable a man in John's condition to make himself understood. This was something that, so far as I could see, would enable him to sing, if his inclinations went that way.

Forthwith I had the apparatus in its special box carried down to my car, and I arranged to meet the engineer at the hospital the next day so that we might give John his first lesson in his new voicebox.

The little group who arrived as visitors, for several other interested people in the factory came with the chief engineer, all eager to see their creation in practical use, surprised John, and he seemed a little dazed at first. But when the idea was explained to him his eyes lighted up. He took his first lesson well, and the nurse too was given instruction so that she could assist him in his practice.

In a few weeks time he had completely mastered the trick of the thing, and as soon as his general health permitted he was reinstated as foreman of the very shop that had made his artificial voice. There is a certain just satisfaction in the thought that he now uses a radio voice to control the production of other types of radio apparatus, used mainly for purposes of war. And I understand that so far from being pitied by his colleagues, he is regarded as blessed beyond all other foremen, for he alone has the power of altering the volume of his voice at will and without any effort. Though he speaks in a mutter, he can, if he chooses, amplify it so that the sound rises above the din of machines. It is a voice that certainly cannot be shouted down.

This, then, was my first direct contact with the engineering world, and my initial attempt at enlisting the active help of those ingenious gentlemen who write strange letters after their names. The results were highly successful, and they open up all manner of speculations on future collaboration of this kind. But the possibilities are, for a surgeon, somewhat frightening. They suggest that in the future he may be expected to add engineering principles to the many things he is expected to know at this present time, and for the medical student the likelihood of adding a section on engineering to his already overburdened course. That is certainly a prospect which fails to fill me with any kind of enthusiasm, for, as I have said, I have not a mechanical mind.

XX

AS FIT AS A FIDDLE

He came to me late in the afternoon. My receptionist had booked the appointment and he had said nothing to her except that he was a new patient. He brought with him no letter of introduction, either from a doctor or a friend. I knew nothing about him whatsoever.

I judged his age as the early fifties. Whatever was the matter with him did not show on the surface. His face was pleasantly tanned, and his dark hair showed no signs of either thinning or of greyness. His grasp, when he shook hands, was firm and friendly. He walked into the room with the balance and poise of a man who has led an active, outdoor life. His eyes were clear and his gaze steady.

Usually one can gather an inkling of a patient's condition from external details before he has spoken a single word or offered any explanation at all. But this man puzzled me completely. I am too old a hand, however, to be taken in by appearances. It is not a mere fantasy that healthy looks often conceal deep-seated disorder.

I asked what was the matter and why he had come.

"A sort of vague uneasiness, doctor," he replied in a musical voice. "I can't explain it. It suggests to me that there is something wrong. I feel I need a thorough overhaul."

"Did you come here on anybody's recommendation?" I asked.

He shook his head. "Someone mentioned your name to me," he replied vaguely. "I can't even remember who it was. But the name stuck and here I am."

"But if you need a general examination, it would surely be better to see a consulting physician. I am a surgeon, you know. My work is just a little specialized."

"I know all about that," he said. "As a matter of fact, I have already seen a physician, and he said I had better see a surgeon, as I had nothing wrong with me so far as he could see."

"Whom did you consult?"

"Dr. Gennifer," he answered.

I made a note of the name. This was something a little more tangible. I knew Gennifer well. He is one of the best of the younger physicians. I would have a word with him about this. I felt pretty certain that if he could find nothing wrong to account for the vague uneasiness of this patient, I should not. Even then the case suggested that what was wanted was a psychiatrist. The man had a delusion of some kind. He was akin to the hypochondriacs who are the curse of a consultant's existence.

I asked him a few more questions, but could tie him down to nothing. No, he felt no pain. The "uneasiness" was not associated with any special part of the body. He was eating and sleeping quite normally. But he still insisted that he wanted my opinion. It would help a lot, he said.

At last, as I had no more appointments that day, I decided to give him a thorough examination. Nothing else would satisfy him, it seemed. He might have some obscure psychological complaint, in which case a reassurance might help him. But I still wondered why Gennifer had sent him to me. It was definitely something I must look into.

I went through the complete box of tricks, to put it irreverently. I tested his heart and his reflexes. I looked into his eyes. I took his blood pressure. I noted the condition of his kidneys and his liver. I tickled the soles of his feet and tapped his knee with an ivory hammer. He seemed highly gratified by these attentions.

Finally I told him to dress. He did so slowly as though reluctant to abandon an experience that had satisfied him in some way. I glanced through my notes. No, there was nothing—nothing at all that I could discover.

"What's the verdict, doctor?" he asked with a touch of anxiety. Perhaps he had misread my silence as a mark of doubt.

"A very good one," I replied. "How old did you say you were?"

"Fifty-three," he answered.

"H'm!" I smiled to myself. "So far as I can discover there is absolutely nothing the matter with you. I have given you a thorough overhaul, and I can determine nothing out of order. All your functions are normal. If I was asked to give an opinion, I should say that you were not only an extremely fit man, but an unusually fit man for your age. I should say that the majority of men at forty-five showed a lower condition than you do."

He beamed. I had expected protests and a reiteration of his theme-song of "uneasiness". But his expression was one of surpassing joy.

"You agree with Dr. Gennifer, then?" he asked.

"Certainly in that I can find nothing wrong with you."

He nodded and produced a small notebook covered in red leather from his pocket.

"And in that you add yours to the unanimous opinion of . . ." and he reeled off a list of five physicians, three surgeons, and two psychiatrists, all of them with names well known in Harley Street. I looked at him in amazement.

"Have you consulted all those people?" I gasped.

"Yes. They all complimented me on my condition. Now confidentially, doctor, and in no way in disparagement of your opinion or that of these other gentlemen"—he tapped the notebook, to the list in which he had added my name before replacing it—"would you consider Dr. de Lusigny a good man to consult?"

"He is one of the finest physicians France has sent us," I replied. "Are you proposing to go to him?"

"The thought occurred to me," he replied, beaming again.

I lost my temper.

"But why—why, man? You've had the best opinions already. There's nothing at all wrong with you. You're wasting time and money—you can do what you like with your own, I suppose, but don't you realize you're wasting doctors' time, which is very valuable?"

The smile did not fade.

"Perhaps. But I am fifty-three, doctor—an age when men start to decline. It is quite a thrill for me to be told by eminent specialists, at the rate of two per month, that I am a thoroughly fit man."

He turned abruptly to the door, that idiotic grin still on his face. I was too staggered to see him out.

EPILOGUE

They came by appointment, and they left by devious ways. Some went away disappointed. Others found all that they sought. Many of them—and this is my greatest joy—have never gone away at all, for they have remained as friends.

Some who thought to find life found only death; and those are the ones whom I remember with sadness. For one never grows callous to the fact of death in one's soul, however outwardly one may seem cold and indifferent. Some discovered the way to a fullness of life they never believed possible; and these cases, while they arouse satisfaction in the heart, promote also humility before the idea that the powers of the surgeon are so great and that so much power rests in human hands.

When they came they were names. Some one had heard of from friends; some were heralded by letters from those sturdy shocktroops of medicine, the general practitioners who keep the flag of health flying in all the corners of the land. But not one of them long remained a name. Each had a story; and it is the story of his life which is the man himself.

These are the tale I have set down as best I may in these pages, telling them not with literary flourishes but with the simple directness that is appropriate to plain men's lives. They, the richest stuff of drama, need no dramatization. It is only the fantasies and paper figures of the novelist's imagination that need to be tricked out with the finery of resplendent words. The simple human tale is the most moving of all; and it is the simple human tale of happiness and woe, of fear and hope, that the doctor hears every day in his consulting room.

As I have written these stories, I have lived through the experiences again, marvelling at the richness of human life.

I have remade old friendships. About some I have wondered, for they have passed beyond my ken. About others I have thought again how strange are the ways by which men come to lasting friendship.

Let there be no talk of all men being cases to the doctor. He does not deal in mass-produced screws or bars of soap. Each one who walks into his room brings with him a world of his own, in which the very values are different from those one has oneself. It is only in the consulting-room that one realizes this fact.

It is a profound and stimulating thought, one of which the surgeon and physician must always be aware, for it means quite simply that one can never treat two people alike. I hope that in reading these stories, the reader may find here or there the same great thought, so that he may never cease to marvel at the life of which he is so infinitesimal a part.